THE POCKET GUIDE
TO MUSHROOMS

Managing editor: Hervé Chaumeton
Project coordination: Muriel Bresson
Design and Layout: Nathalie Lachaud, Jean-François Laurent, Isabelle Véret
Typesetting: Stéphanie Henry, Véronique Janvier, Chantal Mialon

The author and the editorial team would like to acknowledge the kind assistance of René-Jacques Bouteville of the Auvergne Natural History Society, who is also a member of the Societé Mycologique de France, and thank him for his help and advice.

Original title: *Le mini-guide des champignons*

Translation from French: Josephine Bacon, Chanterelle Translations, London
Adaptation of the English edition: Josephine Bacon
Typesetting: Chanterelle Translations, London; Divis, Cologne
Repro studio: Typografik, Cologne
Project coordination: Alex Morkramer
Production: Ursula Schümer
Printing and Binding: Star Standard Industries Ltd.

Printed in Singapore

ISBN 3-8290-2905-5

10 9 8 7 6 5 4 3 2 1

THE POCKET GUIDE TO MUSHROOMS

Jean-Marie Polese

KÖNEMANN

PREFACE

This is a field guide to wild mushrooms, also known as fungi. It does not include all of the species, of course, because there are several thousand of the macrofungi, those which can be seen with the naked eye, but you will find the most frequently found species in this book.

The mushrooms featured here are generally found throughout the temperate zone of the northern hemisphere, though there may be slight variations from one continent to another. A few species have a more restricted habitat but are quite common in those areas in which they grow.

A certain number of species which are especially frequent or which are of particular interest due to their edibility or toxicity are dealt with in greater detail and are more extensively illustrated.

This book will be of interest to the amateur mycologist as well as to the novice mushroom-picker who wants to be able to identify fungi precisely and accurately, and even to the more experienced picker who would like to extend his or her knowledge to other species, whether they are edible or not. In order to give the reader some idea of how mushrooms are classified, we have used the method adopted by French mycologists who are the European authorities.

Shape, color, odor, taste, and habitat are all properties that are unique to each species. It is rare to be able to recognize a species on the basis of one of these factors alone. It is usually a combination of several characteristics that enable identification of a specimen with certainty.

All this makes mycology, the study of fungi, a discipline which increases powers of observation and exercises the critical faculties. It also arouses a sense of wonder and increases feelings of humility when faced with the extraordinary diversity of nature and the amazing creative genius of which the kingdom of the fungi is proof. We hope that this book will lift the veil from certain aspects of the strange and fascinating world of wild mushrooms.

CONTENTS

NOTICE TO READERS

The illustrations and descriptions of
species in this book have been produced
with the greatest care.
If you are in the slightest doubt, however,
as to the edibility of a mushroom, do not
eat it, and consult an identification expert.

H : height
L : length
∅ : diameter

INTRODUCTION

ANATOMY OF A MUSHROOM

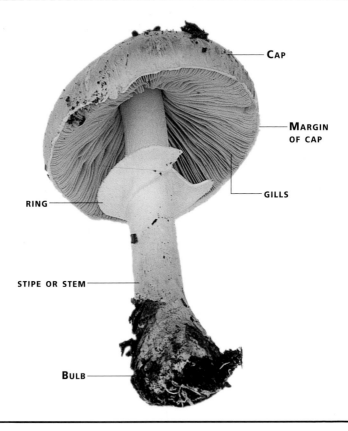

CAP

MARGIN
OF CAP

GILLS

RING

STIPE OR STEM

BULB

METHOD
OF ATTACHMENT
OF GILLS
TO THE STIPE

Adnexed

Adnate

Decurrent

CAP

Convex

Umbonate

Funnel-shaped

Hemispherical

Depressed

Conical

MARGIN OF CAP

Smooth

Enrolled

Undulating or sinuous

Fluted

Striated

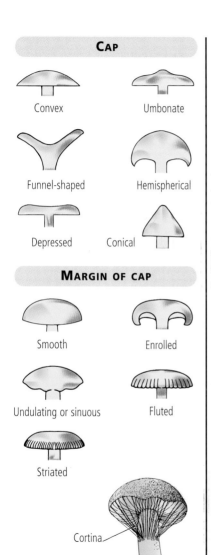

Cortina

TEXTURE AND SHAPE OF STIPE

Fibrillose

Downy

Reticulate

Sinuous

Club-shaped

Bulbous

Thin

Lateral

Excentric

BULB

Marginate

Non-marginate

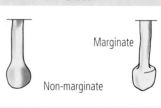

VOLVA

Sac-like

Sheath-like

Ridged bulb

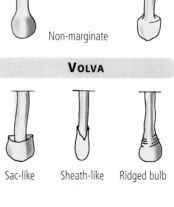

WHAT IS A FUNGUS?

Fungi were once classified as plants, but today they are considered to be in a class of their own, neither vegetable nor animal, inhabitants of the fungal kingdom. Unlike plants, they do not have stems, leaves, or roots. Fungi contain no chlorophyll, the substance that enables plants to manufacture their own food, so they are forced to find food from their environment, in the same way as animals.

The mushroom that is visible is actually just the largest part of an organism most of which lies in the soil, embedded in leaf litter, humus, decaying wood, and similar habitats. A fungus looks like a network of very fine fil-aments, which are called *hyphae*, and which are invisible to the naked eye when found in isolation. However, hyphae often cling together and their density makes them visible in the form of a white, felt-like substance or as thin strings. The mass of hyphae is called a *mycelium*. Mycelia can often be found in early fall beneath the moss which grows on the forest floor. Some mycelia can be found growing over several dead leaves which they clump together. This is the case

The fall is the best time of year for finding and picking mushrooms.

Mycelium has caused the leaves on this branch to clump together

with certain species of Clitocybe. A particularly thick mass of mycelium can sometimes be seen on the pine needles that carpet the floor of coniferous forests, especially spruce. The real function of a fungus is to produce spores, its minute dispersal organs. That is why mycologists call the visible mushroom the fruiting body or *carpophore* (from the Greek *karpos* meaning "fruit" and *phoros* "support" or "bearer"). The fruiting body is also known as a *sporophore* (from the Greek *spora* meaning "seed").

Life cycle of the fungus

A fungus produces spores which, once in the substrate, germinate into a very fine, white filament which branches out in all directions. This primary mycelium is incapable of producing a carpophore on its own. In order for this to happen, the mycelium needs to encounter a filament from another spore of the same species of fungus, but one which is genetically different. The two types of filament merge to create another type of filament, the secondary mycelium, which is fertile and is capable of producing a mushroom. Very often, it takes more than

two types of genetically different spores to produce a fruiting-body; as many as four, may be required, which makes procreation a rather complicated process!

Fungi produce a huge number of spores. The champion in this respect is the Giant Puff-ball, a real spore-making factory. This fungus can exceed 16 inches (40 cm) in diameter. According to an eminent mycologist, a single specimen is capable of releasing 10 billion spores into the atmosphere!

Despite the amazing number of spores produced by fungi, they clearly have not invaded the planet. In fact, in nature, spores very rarely develop a mycelium. For instance, groups of Marasmius oreades, the Fairy Ring Champignon, are to be found every year in abundance in certain meadows, while neighboring meadows, which have the same agricultural, physical, and chemical properties, never have a single specimen, even though spores must have drifted over from the neighboring field and landed there countless times over the years.

Although certain mycelia are known to live for centuries (an example is the abovementioned Fairy Ring Champignon) the mycelium of other species die every year. The cycle then starts over in the spores which germinate in the substrate, producing new filaments and new mycelia, and eventually new carpophores.

How mushrooms are formed

At a certain moment in the life of the filaments, under conditions which are still a mystery, they start to clump together instead of growing in all directions. A little lump then appears on the filaments, a ball of hyphal threads the size of a pinhead. This is called a *primordium* and it is the start of what will become the carpophore of the mushroom. So the carpophore consists of a grouping together of filaments which in other organisms would be comparable to a group of cells combining to form tissue.

Only when the fruiting body is fairly well developed can the species be identified. Mycelium on its own is very hard to attribute to a species, especially with the naked eye.

Although it is often said that mushrooms only grow if they find themselves in a favorable environment, the reverse is actually the case. If mycelium is grown in the laboratory under ideal conditions, it never produces fruiting bodies. Mycelium needs a form of stimulation which will cause it to react and emerge from its vegetative state. If it believes that its survival is under threat, it will produce a response to ensure its continued existence, and this takes the form of a sporophore. The fruiting body will enable the fungus to survive in adversity and germinate

Several species of wild mushrooms that grow in woods are now cultivated commercially. These include the Oyster Mushroom, the Blewit (pictured here), and the Shaggy Ink Cap.

as soon as conditions improve. This phenomenon has been successfully exploited by mushroom-growers. To produce the store or Portobello mushroom, growers cover the substrate which is impregnated with the fungus mycelium with a layer of sandy soil, several inches thick, stimulating the production of fruiting bodies. In the case of Blewits, a wild variety that has only recently been cultivated, the triggering factor is a sudden drop in temperature.

A lovely forest in glorious fall weather is an invitation to go mushroom-hunting.

ECOLOGY

Fungi are normally divided into three categories depending on where they find their food and their behavior in the growing environment.

– **Saprophytic fungi** feed on dead organic vegetable matter (leaves, twigs, logs, etc.) or animal remains (carrion, excreta). This is the case, for instance, with all the fungi that grow on dead tree trunks or logs, such as the Honey Fungus, those which grow on dead leaves, such as the Blewit, or the weird-looking Ear-pick Fungus, which grows on fallen pine cones. Fungi play a very important role in the decomposition of all types of waste and in the formation of humus which enriches the soil. Some microscopic saprophitic fungi are valuable aids in the fields of medicine and food preparation.

The Blewet is a saprophyte which grows on oak or beech leaves.

Penicillin is extracted from a *Penicillium notatum;* yeast, used in brewing and baking, is also a type of fungus.

– **Parasitic fungi** grow on living plants and animals and thrive at their expense. The most frequently encountered species are Polypores or the fungi that form a lichen-like crust on the trunks or branches of living trees. The spores find their way into a wound where they germinate or they

Saprophytic fungi play an important role in nature, by cleaning up dead trees and plant debris.

attack a host in a weakened state and kill it. Numerous species of fungi are both parasites and saprophytes, because they continue to feed off a host even after they have killed it. This is the case with two tree parasites, the Tinder Fungus, also known as the Hoof Fungus (*Fomes fomentarius*) and the Honey Fungus (*Armillaria mellea*). Such fungi are even capable of living an entirely saprophytic existence, only invading wood when it is dead. The microscopic fungi or molds which cause plant diseases, such as rust, smut, wilt, and mildew to such devastating effect are also parasites. Fungal diseases of animals are called mycoses. The commonest in humans are Athlete's Foot and Ringworm.

– **The mycorrhizal fungi.** These are fungi that live in symbiosis with a plant, generally a tree. Symbiosis is a system in which two living beings live off each other to their mutual advantage. The mycelium combines with the rootlets of the plant, which take on a swollen appearance. The resulting combination of root and mycelium is called a mycorrhiza, a Latin word which literally means "fungus-root." It is in the mycorrhiza that the exchange of nutrients takes place. The plant supplies the mushroom with carbohydrates resulting from photosynthesis. In exchange, the fungus feeds the green plant with water and mineral salts, especially those which the plant finds hardest to convert from the soil, such as nitrates. It is able to do this because of its dense network of mycelial filaments which are in closer contact with the soil than the rootlets of plants. It thus creates a sort of extension of the rootlets, increasing the area of contact between the soil and the rootlets. Symbiosis is not confined to trees but is practiced by many other plants, including heather, orchids, and even cereals. In fact, three-

This strange, long, thin fungus is a species of Cordyceps, Cordyceps ophioglossoides. *It parasitizes other fungi, in this case a subterranean truffle-like fungus called* Elaphomyces muricatus *or Deer Truffle.*

quarters of all green plants benefit from a mycorrhizal association. Some, such as orchids, are even incapable of life without it. The system of exchanges enables the green plants that benefit from it to grow quickly and strongly. Experiments conducted by many research organizations show that saplings, in particular, derive great advantage from a symbiotic association with a fungus.

The fungi even participate actively in protecting the tree by releasing chemicals into the soil which prevent attack by predators and pests. Some fungi have even been shown to create nets of mycelium in which

*Mycorrhyzal fungi are sometimes associated with a single species, such as the Elegant Bolete (*Suillus grevillei*) which only lives under larch.*

to trap and destroy the nematodes (tiny worms) and other insect pests that gnaw away at the rootlets of plants and seriously damage, stunt, or kill them.

In exchange for the great service rendered by the mycorrhizal fungus, the plant or tree supplies the fungus with organic matter which it is incapable of producing by itself.

MUSHROOMS AND MAN

Man has always been curious about and fascinated with fungi. The mystery surrounding their growth, the way they appear so suddenly (Shakespeare's "midnight mushrooms"), the strange circles which are formed by some species in meadows or forest clearings, and the violent reactions they can cause to the human organism, including serious poisoning and even death, have inspired fear and superstition. Even today, many people have a phobia about wild mushrooms, despite the fact that fungal Fly Agaric (*Amanita muscaria*), for instance has been used since at least the eighteenth century in the rituals of native peoples of Siberia, North America, and Lapland.

Some Nordic tribes have taken advantage of the hallucinogenic substances found in Fly Agaric (Amanita muscaria).

Fairy rings of mushrooms have given rise to many tales and beliefs.

Some mushrooms, such as this Liberty Cap (Psilocybe semilanceata) are hallucinogenic.

In central America and Mexico, hallucinogenic fungi of the genus Psilocybe were used by the priests of pre-Columbian civilizations. They may well have been sacred or even deified, as certain figurines and representations of the mushroom would appear to indicate.

Mushrooms must have played quite an important role in the diet of early man. They are still eaten in abundance, but generally as a flavoring or delicacy, though vegetarians appreciate them as a meat substitute.

The Tinder Fungus and similar woody species probably enabled our ancestors to preserve fire and carry it around with them. This fungus burns very slowly and retains an incandescent spot. At a later date, it was used in tinder boxes, hence its name. The Styptic Fungus (*Panellus stypticus*) was used in staunching wounds, as the name implies. Fungi have also been harnessed to industry. They are indispensable in

The decorative properties of Coriolus versicolor *are used in flower-arranging.*

making bread, cheeses, alcohol, penicillin, and many other useful items. The corky flesh of the Birch Polypore (*Piptoporus betulinus*) was used to make a leathery substance on which barbers sharpened their cut-throat razors, hence its old-fashioned name, the Razor-Strop Fungus.

Thus quite apart from their food value, fungi are employed in various areas of human endeavor, including the arts and flower-arranging. The Many-Zoned Polypore (*Coriolus versicolor*) is often used in dried flower arrangements, as are some members of the Pleurotus family which are cultivated for their bright colors.

If mixed with potassium nitrate, the Tinder Fungus will burst into flame when struck to produce a spark.

Fungi also have many negative aspects, in that they can ravage crops, cause illness in humans and animals, and destroy any type of vegetable matter that is not carefully stored.

The mold which is used to make blue cheese is the mycelium of a fungus called Penicillium roquefortii.

PICKING AND EATING

One of the best-known properties of fungi is the edibility of certain mushrooms. In some parts of the world, including central and eastern Europe, Turkey, and North America, fungi are assiduously collected for the table. Whether they are to be eaten at home or picked for sale to markets and restaurants, the number of wild mushrooms currently picked has reached a tonnage that actually surpasses that of cultivated mushrooms such as the store or Portobello mushroom, the Paddy Straw Mushroom, and Shiitake Mushrooms consequently play a significant part in the human diet. They are eaten throughout the world from the cold countries to the tropics of Africa and Asia.

Mushroom consumption is patchy, however, depending on the country or region and local tradition and custom. In Southeast Asia, for instance, especially Indonesia, the Philippines, and China, mushrooms have been eaten for centuries. In these countries, mushroom-growing is a cottage industry. Indonesia is the world's biggest producer of Paddy Straw Mushrooms (*Volvariella volvacea*). In China, many fungi are used in Chinese medicine. In Africa, the most popular edible mushrooms are of the species Termitomyces, which grow on termite nests.

Europe is divided into two camps, the countries which reject wild fungi and those that eat them with relish. The former group consists mainly of the United Kingdom and Scandinavia, as well as parts of Spain (though the Spanish eat the Saffron Milk Cap). The latter group includes several western European countries, especially France, Italy, Germany, and Switzerland, as well as the countries of central and Eastern Europe. In France, for example, consumption amounts to several kilograms of wild mushrooms per person per year. Eastern Europe has a very

Every fall, an abundance of wild mushrooms appear on market stalls in Europe.

ancient tradition of gathering wild mushrooms and a large number of species is eaten. Some, such as the Peppery Milk Cap (*Lactarius piperatus*) considered inedible elsewhere, are used as seasonings.

Rules for picking wild mushrooms

For eating purposes, only pick those wild mushrooms that you have identified with certainty. It is best to pick them before they are fully mature, but beware of those which are very young, whose shape and color could be interpreted in various ways.

Young specimens, recognizable by the firmness of their flesh, are much tastier than older ones. Younger mushrooms stay firmer during cooking and are less likely to be worm-eaten.

A fungus foray in the forest in search of chanterelles.

The mushroom-pickers equipment is very simple, consisting merely of a stick, a sharp knife, a basket and sharp eyes.

or you will be disturbing the medium on which the mycelium grows and may kill the fungus. If you are careful to pick mushrooms without disturbing their growing medium, you will not compromise their future growth. Mycelium present in the soil could produce another specimen during the same growing season or in the following year.

Try not to mix different species in the same basket. Those with fragile flesh should be

Some species must be removed whole from the ground, with their stipe and base, in order to avoid any danger of mistaken identity (such as confusing the Blusher with the Panther Cap). Otherwise, fungi should be cut away at ground level with a knife. In the case of fungi which are easily recognizable but whose stipe is too tough to eat, such as the Parasol Mushroom (*Macrolepiota procera*), only the cap should be picked.

Before placing the mushroom in your basket, remove any dirt or debris clinging to it. Try and bring home a harvest of mushrooms which are as insect-free and clean as possible, because as will be explained later, it is best to avoid washing mushrooms before cooking them.

Do not scratch around or dig up the dirt around a mushroom, or root around disturbing moss or dead leaves to find specimens,

In places that only they can reach, children love to go looking for mushrooms.

separated from firm, fleshy species which might crush them and reduce them to an inedible pulp.

Mushroom cuisine

Mushrooms ought to be eaten as soon as possible after they have been picked. Most species can be stored in the refrigerator for several days, however.

Preparation

It is not advisable to wash mushrooms, as this may remove some of the flavor. For those species which do not need much cleaning, it is best to pick them as cleanly as possible and scrape off any dirt with a knife, then wipe them with a damp cloth.

If washing cannot be avoided (as in the case of the Horn of Plenty, and other species that grow in sand), this should be done as quickly as possible, and above all do not leave mushrooms to soak in water. Drain them on a kitchen towel or kitchen paper.

Cooking methods

As regards the best way to cook them, opinions are very divided. Some cooks simmer wild mushrooms for an hour or so, while others consider that they should be cooked quickly over high heat. It is all a matter of taste, though it also depends on the texture of the mushroom itself. Fleshy species, such as Ceps and Chanterelles, can withstand long cooking, those with thin, fragile flesh,

The next scene after a fruitful fungus foray in the forest is set in the kitchen.

such as the Ink Caps, the Blusher and the Grisette should be quickly fried in very hot oil; if subjected to long, slow cooking, they will turn into an unappetising mush.

As a general rule, the first stage of cooking consists in making the mushrooms release the water they contain by heating them in a skillet or pan that is large enough to ensure even cooking, simply to allow the water to evaporate. This operation does not require the addition of fat, but a tablespoon of oil

could be used to prevent the mushrooms sticking to the pan. Mushrooms release varying quantities of liquid, depending on the species and on whether or not they have been washed. The Cep, for example, is a fleshy fungus which does not need to be washed, releases very little liquid.

The second stage consists in sautéing mushrooms over high heat in a mixture of oil and butter. Some people used a strongly flavored oil, such as olive oil, and in France duck fat

These Ceps have been dried and stored in Mason jars. They will keep for several months.

is sometimes used. Another method of cooking the mushrooms is to braise them in a covered pan.

Gastronomy is not an exact science and it is up to the individual to discover the best ways to cook their favorite species of mushroom. Now that wild mushrooms are becoming so popular on restaurant menus, and species once only to be found in the wild are now being cultivated, it is becoming easier all the time to find recipes for cooking fungi. Perhaps the only rule is that they should not be cooked with any food, such as cheese, which masks their subtle flavors. The reduction in price also makes it easier to experiment. Furthermore, those who are nervous about not washing specimens found in the wild will prefer the cultivated versions, which are always grown on a sterile substrate, and thus are free of contamination.

IDENTIFICATION KEY

FUNGI WITH AN UNDIFFERENTIATED CAP	Spherical or globular mushroom, sometimes developing into diverse forms	Not subterranean	Globular
			Phallus-shaped
			Star-shaped
		Subterranean	
	Fungi in the shape of cups, antlers, or pustules		
	Club-shaped fungi, branched, bushy fungi, neither viscous nor gelatinous		
	Viscous or gelatinous fungus Fungus spreading in a crust or fans-shaped fungus.		

	GASTEROMYCETES	Puff-balls (fragile skin), Scleroderma (leathery skin) **p. 356 to p. 361**
	GASTEROMYCETES	Phallus **p. 363 to p. 364**
	GASTEROMYCETES	Geaster anthurus **p. 354 to p. 355** **p. 364 to p. 365**
	ASCOMYCETES	Truffles **p. 56 to p. 57**
	ASCOMYCETES	Xylaria hypoxylon, Bisporella citrina, Peziza spp. **p. 34 to p. 45**
	APHYLLOPHORALES	Clavairia **p. 99 to p. 105**
	PHRAGMOBASIDOMYCETES	Exidia, Auricularia, Tremella… **p. 60 to p. 62**
	APHYLLOPHORALES	Stereum, Trametes, Polypores… **p. 66 to p. 85**

FUNGI WITH A DIFFERENTIATED CAP	Fungus with pores in place of gills	Central, differentiated stipe, ground grower.	
		Lateral or absent stipe, growing on wood or on the ground	
	Fungus with spines in place of gills	Gelatinous flesh	
		Non-gelatinous flesh	
	Fungi with a pitted or deeply lobed cap		
	Trumpet-or funnel-shaped fungus, underside smooth or covered in decurrent veins		
	Mushroom with flesh separable from the cap and decurrent gills.		

	BOLETALES	Boletus, Suillus, Xerocomus, Tylopilus **p. 318 to p. 344**
	APHYLLOPHORALES	Polypores **p. 80 to p. 85**
	PHRAGMOBASIDIOMYCÈTES	Hydnum gelatinosum **p. 63**
	APHYLLOPHORALES	Hydnum **p. 86 to p. 89**
	ASCOMYCETES	Helvella, Verpa, Morchella **p. 46 to p. 55**
	APHYLLOPHORALES	Cantharellus, Craterellus **p. 90 to p. 98**
	BOLETALES	Gomphidius, Paxillus **p. 345 to p. 348**

Mushroom whose gills are not separable from the flesh of the cap	Brittle stipe	
	Fibrous stipe	Spores white or cream, gills the same color but sometimes yellow, orange, or violet.
		Spores pink, gills pinkish at maturity.
		Spores sepia brown or black, gills blackish at maturity
		Spores ocher brown, rust or brown-violet, gills the same color at maturity

	RUSSULALES	Russula (no milk), Lactarius (milky substance appears when damaged) **p. 286 to p. 315**
Non-separable stipe	**TRICHOMATALES**	Hygrophorus, Pleurotus, Lentinus, Lentinellus, Clitocybe, Tricholoma, Lepista, Armillaria, Melanoleuca, Collybia, Marasmius, Mycena **p. 108 to p. 177**
	BOLETALES	Clitocybe nebularis, Pleurotus ostreatus, Clitocybe aurantiaca **p. 349 to p. 351**
Stipe separable	**AGARICALES**	Agaricus, Lepiota, Amanita **p. 190 to p. 229**
	ENTOLOMATALES	Clitopilus, Entoloma, Pluteus (no ring or volva), Volvaria (volva but no ring) **p. 232 to p. 239**
	AGARICALES	Psathyrella, Coprinus **p. 180 to p. 190**
	CORTINARIALES	Paneolus **p. 281 to p. 283**
	CORTINARIALES	Cortinarius,Hebeloma, Inocybe, Pholiota, Stropharia, Hypholoma, Psilocybe, Agrocybe **p. 242 to p. 283**

THE ASCOMYCETES

CORDYCEPS OPHIOGLOSSOIDES

Club-shaped Cordyceps

DESCRIPTION: H:1¼-3¼ in (4-8 cm). Shaped like a club with a swollen, granulose and blackish tip, which when mature is covered with a whitish powder.

HABITAT: deciduous or coniferous woods in the fall. Fairly frequent but often passes unnoticed.

SPECIAL CHARACTERISTICS

Cordyceps are all formidable parasites. In some species, the mycelium develops in the bodies of insects or their larvae, causing them to die. The bright-red *Cordyceps militaris* kills flies in this way. The Club-shaped Cordyceps parasitizes a type of truffle with a yellow mycelium. The same family includes crop pests such as ergot of rye (*Claviceps purpurea*).

NECTRIA CINNABARINA

Scarlet Nectria

DESCRIPTION: Ø:0.08-0.4 in (0.2-0.5 cm).
This fungus has two distinct forms, that of smooth, pink pillows or cinnabar red, hard, granulose pustules. The two forms are frequently found together.

HABITAT: on the dead branches of a variety of deciduous trees. Found all year round, but mainly in the fall. Very common.

THE ASCOMYCETES

XYLARIA HYPOXYLON
Candle-snuff Fungus

DESCRIPTION: H: 1/8-3 in (1-8 cm).
Fruiting bodies resemble little stag horns, almost cylindrical at first, then flattened, black at the base and white at the top. Flesh has a corky consistency.

HABITAT: logs and the dead branches of deciduous trees. Found all year round, but mainly in winter. Very common.

HYPOXYLON FRAGIFORME
Strawberry Hypoxylon

DESCRIPTION: Ø: 1/8-1/2 in (0.5-1 cm).
Small granulose globules, brick red at first then blackening. Blackish-brown, coriaceous flesh.

HABITAT: on bark or dead branches of beech trees. Different stages may be present at the same time. Found all year round, but mainly in winter. Very common.

USTULINA DEUSTA
Burnt Ustilina

DESCRIPTION:
Ø:³/₄-4in (2-10 cm).
Grayish when young, then devel
oping into black, granulose, brittle
lumps ¹/₁₆ to ¹/₄ in (2 to 5 mm) thick.

HABITAT: on decomposing beech
logs. Common. Lives for several
years. The pale gray areas of
growth appear in late spring or
summer, then blacken and persist from one year to the next.

SCLEROTINIA TUBEROSA, DUMONTINIA TUBEROSA
Tuberous Sclerotinia

DESCRIPTION: H:1¹/₂-4 in (4-10 cm), Ø:¹/₂-
1¹/₄ in (1-3 cm).
Receptacle at first deeply cup-shaped then
shallower, brown or hazelnut. Stipe brown,
long but partly embedded in the soil, sinuous and attached to a black sclerotium.

HABITAT: damp woods, hedgerows, and
meadows alongside wood anemones and
Ranunculaceae such as lesser celandine.
Common.

SPECIAL CHARACTERISTICS

This fungus attaches itself via a sclerotium to the dead roots of the host
plant. It is a hard, black spherical mass
measuring about ¹/₂ in (1 cm) and repre-
senting a resistant form of the fungus.

BULGARIA INQUINANS

Bachelor's Button

DESCRIPTION: Ø: $^1/_4$-$1^1/_2$ in (0.5-4 cm). Globulose at first, then widening and becoming slightly cup-shaped, the center become smooth and shiny with bluish high- lights. It becomes covered with a black dust (the black spores of the fungus) which stains the fingers. The outer part is brown, velvety and granulose. The flesh is ocher-brown, elastic, and rubbery.

SPECIAL CHARACTERISTICS

The same species of tree is host to the Truncated Bulgaria *(Bulgaria truncata)*, which is a close relative of Bachelor But- ton but its spores do not stain the fin- gers.

HABITAT: grows in patches on bark or branches of oak, chestnut, and beech that have recently been cut down. Fall and win- ter. Common.

ASCOCORYNE SARCOIDES

Fleshy Ascocoryne

DESCRIPTION:
Ø: $^1/_4$-$^5/_8$ in (0.5-1.5 cm). The fruiting body is cup- or fun- nel-shaped with a flattened or convex top, which becomes con- cave. Violet-pink or purple-red gelatinous flesh, margin often lobed. Stipe absent or very short.

HABITAT: in large, tightly packed clumps on rotting dead wood, especially beech, but also fir. Fall and winter. Common.

NEOBULGARIA PURA

Pale Bachelor's Button

DESCRIPTION: Ø:¹/₂-1¹/₂ in (1-4 cm).
Conical, fleshy, and gelatinous, almost
translucent. The upper side is smooth
with a slightly raised margin. The
underside is smooth, beige or pinkish.

HABITAT: on the bark of branches of
deciduous trees that have died recently,
especially beech. Grows in tight clumps.
From summer through late fall. Fairly
common.

CHLOROCIBORIA AERUGINASCENS, CHLOROSPLENIUM AERUGINASCENS

Blue-green Wood Cup

DESCRIPTION: Ø:¹/₄-¹/₂ in (0.5-1 cm).
A small, wide shallow cup with a wavy margin, on a short stipe. The fungus is entirely
blue-green in color, with a slightly paler
exterior; very often the wood around it is
stained blue-green.

HABITAT: grows in colonies on dead
wood with no bark (oak, hazelnut, beech).
Found all year round. The fungus fruits
quite rarely, but the blue-green mycelium
forms large distinctive patches on tree
trunks or branches.

BISPORELLA CITRINA
Yellow Bisporella

DESCRIPTION: Ø:0.04-$\frac{1}{8}$ in (0.1-0.3 cm). Looks like a tiny, shallow cup at first; later, the top becomes convex. Bright sulfur yellow in color, turning orange as it ages.

HABITAT: in large colonies on branches stripped of bark, especially beech and hazelnut. Summer through late fall. Common.

LEOTIA LUBRICA
Yellow Nail Fungus

DESCRIPTION: H:1$\frac{1}{4}$-2$\frac{1}{2}$ in (3-6 cm), Ø:$\frac{1}{2}$-$\frac{3}{4}$ in (1-2 cm).
This fungus is completely covered in slime and is the shape of a nail. The edge of the cap is inrolled, irregular, sometimes de-pressed in the center, yellow-brown or yellow-ocher, turning faintly olive with age. Stipe finely granulose, sometimes fluted, pale yellow to ocher. Flesh gelatinous and rubbery, yellow, devoid of odor and taste.

HABITAT: grows singly or in small groups on moss or leaf litter in damp wood. Found in summer through fall. Fairly common.

TOXICITY

Suspected of being poisonous. This fungus could be confused with a young specimen of the Tubular Chanterelle, which is similar in shape and color.

POTENTIAL CONFUSION

▶ *CANTHARELLUS TUBAEFORMIS*
Tubular Chanterelle   EDIBLE

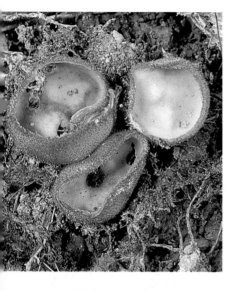

HUMARIA HEMISPHAERICA
Acorn Elf Cup

DESCRIPTION: H:$^1/_2$-$^5/_8$ in (1-1.5 cm), Ø:$^1/_2$-1$^1/_4$ in (1-3 cm).
Looks like an acorn cup, and is sometimes half-buried in leaf litter. Remains semicircular even when mature. The interior of the cup is smooth and shiny, bluish-white to gray-white, then pale ocher. The exterior and margin are covered with thick, dense reddish or brown hairs which are darker at the edge. The flesh is pale and persistent.

HABITAT: grows on the ground, on rotting wood in cool, shady undergrowth. From summer through early fall. Quite common.

SCUTELLINIA SCUTELLATA
Shield-shaped Elf Cup

DESCRIPTION: Ø:0.2-$^1/_2$ in (0.4-1 cm).
A fairly regularly shaped shallow cup without a stipe. The inside is bright reddish-orange and the outside beige and velvety. The margin is covered in blackish-brown hairs $^1/_{32}$-$^1/_{16}$ in (1 to 2 mm) long. The cup is folded inward at first, then flattens out with age. The flesh is reddish, with no particular odor or taste.

HABITAT: in dense clumps on wood, sometimes on soil rich in humus; in very humid places, often beside water. From spring through fall. Common.

TARZETTA CATINUS, PUSTULARIA CATINUS

Crucible Elf Cup

DESCRIPTION: Ø:³/₄-2 in (2-5 cm). Another elf cup that looks like an acorn cup, though in this one the edge is curled over until maturity, and when it opens it exhibits tiny rounded indentations on the margin.

The interior surface is smooth and ochraceous. The outer surface is paler, sometimes almost white, and covered with a very fine down. Short, thin stipe, usually buried in the substrate. Flesh thin and brittle.

SPECIAL FEATURES

This is the largest fungus in the genus *Tarzetta*. Another common species, the Cup-shaped Peziza *(Tarzetta cupularis)* is less than ³/₄ in (2 cm) in diameter.

HABITAT: on bare ground in deciduous or coniferous woods and in gardens. Usually grows in groups, the specimens may be separated or tightly packed together. Fruits in summer. Fairly common.

SARCOSPHAERA CRASSA
Crown Elf Cup

edges. The interior is pinkish-violet, soon turning brown. Outer surface whitish. Whitish flesh $\frac{1}{4}$ in (0.5 cm) thick and brittle; no particular odor or flavor.

HABITAT: under beech trees or pine trees, especially at the edge of woodland paths or roads. Fruits in spring. Uncommon to fairly common.

DESCRIPTION: H:$2\frac{1}{2}$-$4\frac{1}{2}$ in (6-12 cm), Ø: 4-7 in (10-18 cm).
Globular at first and half-buried, the Crown Elf Cup then opens at the top with a wide crown-shaped aperture, with saw-toothed

TOXICITY

Very poisonous when raw, perhaps even deadly. Edible if thoroughly cooked, but in view of its toxicity, it is wiser not to try eating it, even cooked.

SARCOSCYPHA COCCINEA
Scarlet Elf Cup

DESCRIPTION: Ø:$\frac{3}{4}$-2 in (2-5 cm).
This cup with its irregular margin is split in places. The inner surface is bright red. The outer surface is paler and covered with a fine white down. Stipe $\frac{1}{2}$-$\frac{3}{4}$ in (1-2 cm) long, and the same color as the outer surface. Thin, leathery, pink flesh; no particular taste or odor.

HABITAT: grows in large colonies on dead branches and twigs, sometimes half-hidden in moss, often in hedgerows, on bramble or

blackthorn twigs, and in the undergrowth of deciduous woods. Fruits from spring through to winter. Fairly common.

ALEURIA AURANTIA

Orange Peel Fungus

DESCRIPTION:

Ø:½-4 in (1-10 cm).
This Elf Cup has no stipe. The edge
is inrolled when young, flattening
out when older and becoming
wavy or lobed. The inner surface is bright orange, and the
outer surface is pale
orange, and covered
with a fine down. The
flesh is thin and friable,
with no particular odor
or taste.

HABITAT: on bare
ground, dirt roads,
embankments and
freshly turned earth. Found
mainly on clay soil.
Sometimes grows in tightly packed clumps.
Fall to early winter. Very common.

EDIBILITY

This is the only Elf Cup that is edible
raw. All the rest, with a couple of
exceptions, are poisonous raw and must
be cooked to be eaten. However, the
Orange Peel Fungus is not particularly
tasty. Its main interest lies in its brilliant
color that looks good in salads and even
in desserts.

PEZIZA VESICULOSA
Bladder Elf Cup

DESCRIPTION: Ø:1½-4½ in (4-12 cm). Globulose at first, often compressed sideways. It opens out into a wide cup with an inrolled, toothed edge. The smooth inner surface is ocher or fawn. There are often tiny bladders in the bottom of the cup, hence the name. The outer surface is the same color as the inner, though often paler and finely granulose. The flesh is fragile, brittle and whitish, without any special odor or taste.

HABITAT: on rich soil and burnt ground, old compost, and rotting straw. Grows isolated or in tight groups, from spring through fall. Fairly common.

EDIBILITY/TOXICITY
Poisonous when raw. Quite good to eat when thoroughly cooked.

PEZIZA SUCCOSA
Juicy Elf Cup

DESCRIPTION: Ø:½-2 in (1-5 cm). An irregular-shaped cup with an incurving margin. There is no stipe. The inner surface is smooth, ocher or hazelnut in color. The outer surface is paler, sometimes even cream-colored, lightly granulose and pruinose. The flesh is white and tough, exuding a white, milky liquid. The flesh and milk turn yellow a few minutes after cutting.

HABITAT: under deciduous trees, beside paths, on damp, clay soils. Summer and fall. Fairly common.

PEZIZA BADIA
Black Elf Cup

DESCRIPTION: Ø:$^1/_2$-3 in (2-8 cm).
This Elf Cup has no stipe and an irregular, wavy edge. The interior is reddish-brown, then greenish brown. The exterior is also reddish-brown and finely granulose. The flesh is thin, brownish-red, and contains a watery liquid.

HABITAT: On bare soil, beside paths, in clearings and very damp places on acid

EDIBILITY/TOXICITY
Poisonous raw, edible when cooked.

sandy or clay soil. Summer and fall. Common, especially in the south.

OTIDEA ONOTICA
Ear-Jack Fungus

DESCRIPTION: H:1$^1/_4$-4 in (3-10 cm).
Shaped like the ear of a donkey or a hare. The inner surface is ocher or pinkish-yellow. The outer surface is velvety, bright yellow or orange yellow, and acquires rust-colored or brown spots with age. Very short stipe covered in white down. Very thin, elastic flesh.

HABITAT: in small groups under deciduous trees, or sometimes conifers in late summer and fall. Fairly common in places.

HELVELLA ACETABULUM
Cup-Shaped Brain Fungus

DESCRIPTION: H:1¼-2¾ in (3-7 cm),
Ø: 1¼-2¾ in (3-7 cm).
The fungus is shaped like a chalice, with a
brownish-red interior. The outer surface is
paler and slightly velvety. The stipe is short,
though it can be as long as 2 in (5 cm). It
is thickly veined, and sometimes the veins
are ramified, right up to the cup. Flesh elastic then brittle; faint odor and mild flavor.

HABITAT: in groups in well-lit deciduous
woods beside paths, on plains and mountains. Prefers non-acid sandy soil. Found
from spring through early summer. Fairly
common.

SPECIAL FEATURES
Sometimes known as the Vinegar Brain
Fungus because the Romans are said to
have used it like a vinegar bottle.

EDIBILITY/TOXICITY
Poisonous raw, edible cooked.

HELVELLA CRISPA
Common Brain Fungus

DESCRIPTION: H:1¼-4½ in (3-12 cm),
Ø: 1¼-3¼ in (3-8 cm).
This fungus varies considerably in size. The
cap is very irregular, then but curved and
curled. It is cream to pale ocher in color.
Stipe white and hollow, deeply furrowed.
Flesh elastic and thin; faint odor.

HABITAT: deciduous or coniferous woods,
especially borders, footpaths, clearings, and
in meadows beside woods. On calcareous
soil. Late summer and fall. Fairly common.

EDIBILITY/TOXICITY
Poisonous raw, edible cooked.

HELVELLA ELASTICA
Elastic Brain Fungus

DESCRIPTION: H:$2^{1}/_{2}$-4 in (6-10 cm), Ø:$^{3}/_{4}$-$1^{1}/_{2}$ in (2-4 cm).
Undulating, saddle-shaped cap, often consisting of two lobes, cream to pale ocher underside smooth and whitish. Stipe smooth, whitish, elongated and thickened at the base, often compressed and hollow, $1^{1}/_{4}$ to 2 in (3 to 5 mm) in diameter. The elastic flesh has no odor or flavor.

HABITAT: under deciduous trees, on the ground sometimes on rotten logs. Calcareous soil. Fall. Fairly common.

TOXICITY

Poisonous when raw. The Brain Funguses generally make poor eating, and their flesh is elastic and tough.

HELVELLA LACUNOSA
Elfin Saddle or Black Brain Fungus

DESCRIPTION: H:$1^{1}/_{4}$-4 in (3-10 cm).
Very variable in shape, looking very much like the Common Brain Fungus but with a gray-brown to black cap consisting of two or three lobes. The underside is pale gray.

HABITAT: grows in the same places as the Common Brain Fungus, but may persist into the fall. Common and widespread through the temperate and cool zones of both hemispheres.

GYROMITRA ESCULENTA

False Morel

DESCRIPTION: H:2-4¹/₂ in (5-12 cm), Ø:2-4 in (5-10 cm).

Irregular, heavily convoluted cap, looking like a brain, wider than it is tall and reddish-brown in color. The short thick stem is swollen at the base, whitish and hollow. The thin white flesh has a rather fruity odor.

POTENTIAL CONFUSION

▶ *MORCHELLA ESCULENTA*
  Morel   EDIBLE
▶ *PTYCHOVERPA BOHEMICA*
  Bohemian Verpa   EDIBLE

HABITAT: the False Morel is rarely found at heights of less than 1,700 ft (500 m). It appears from late March through May, and as late as June at high altitudes. It lives in coniferous woods, especially well-lit ones, such as clearings and beside paths; rarer under deciduous trees. Prefers cool, damp, rather acid soil. Common in eastern Europe.

brownish-red cap shaped like a brain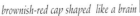

SPECIAL FEATURES

There are other species of Gyromitra (False Morel) which are rare in Europe but more common in North America. The Turban Brain Fungus *(Gyromitra infula)* is a large mountain species with a brownish-yellow to reddish-brown cap which can reach a height of 8 in (20 cm). It grows in the fall in coniferous or mixed woods. The cap consists of two or three lobes, making it look more like a Brain Fungus. The Giant False Morel *(Gyromitra gigas)* is another large species that grows at high altitudes. The cap is reddish-brown to dark brown and less convoluted than that of the False Morel. It can measure 8 in (20 cm) in diameter and grows in late spring.

TOXICITY

Although the False Morel has long been eaten in many countries, especially those of eastern Europe, it can be deadly. Its toxicity is extremely variable, however. Some people have been poisoned who had eaten the mushroom for years without incident. Sometimes, the poison does not manifest itself the first time the fungus is eaten, but only produces symptoms the next time it is consumed, especially if this is soon afterward. Children are particularly vulnerable. When dried, the mushroom is much less toxic, and may even be harmless. Caution is strongly advised, however.

VERPA CONICA

The Glove-Finger Morel

DESCRIPTION: H:2-6 in (5-15 cm), Ø:$\frac{1}{2}$-1$\frac{1}{4}$ in (1-3 cm). The cap is shaped like a truncated cone, and is reminiscent of a thimble on a finger. It is wrinkled and convoluted, sometimes slightly umbilicate at the top. The color varies from brownish-ocher to reddish-brown. The stipe is cylindrical, sometimes thickened at the base. It is short at first, then elongated, sometimes exceeding 4$\frac{1}{2}$ in (12 cm) in length, with a diameter of $\frac{1}{2}$ in (1 cm). It is white, sometimes with a pinkish tinge, and may have wavy lines of hairs across it at intervals. The interior is filled with a cottony fiber at first, later becoming hollow. The flesh is soft and fragile with a faint odor and mild flavor.

HABITAT: grows in troops in spring, in hedgerows and under spiny bushes, such as blackthorn and hawthorn and beneath willow and ash. Favors sandy or gravely limestone. Fairly uncommon.

EDIBILITY/TOXICITY

Poisonous when raw, not particularly good to eat when cooked.

PTYCHOVERPA BOHEMICA

Bohemian Verpa

DESCRIPTION: H:2-8 in (5-20 cm), Ø:³/₄-2 in (2-5 cm).
Conical cap rounded at the top, entirely free (only the top of the cap is attached to the stipe). It consists of thick, longitudinal, ribs, folded into shallow, narrow, irregular honeycomb. The color is ocher to reddish-brown. The stipe is short at first, then extending, sometimes to more than 8 in (20 cm), with a diameter of no less than

stem attached to top of cap

³/₄ in (2 cm). It is fragile and cylindrical, stuffed with cottony fibers at first, then hollow. It is white, tinted with ocher in places and may have bands of whitish down encircling it. The flesh is thin and fragile with a slight odor, that becomes unpleasant with age.

hollow stipe

cells of honeycomb are narrow and shallow

HABITAT: in groups in groves of ash, hazelnut or poplar, especially at mid-mountain height, and often alongside Morels. Grows from mid-March to early May. Uncommon to common.

EDIBILITY/TOXICITY

Poisonous raw, but good cooked.

MITROPHORA SEMILIBERA

Miniature Morel

DESCRIPTION: H:2-6 in (5-15 cm), Ø:¹/₂-1¹/₄ in (1-3 cm).
Cap conical and pointed, rather small, (1¹/₂ to 4 cm) tall. The lower third or half of the cap is not attached to the stem. It is pitted with deep ocher-brown pockets, separated by thin, darker walls which blacken with age. The hollow, cylindrical stem expands slightly under the cap. The white color is sometimes tinted with pale ocher. It is finely grained and often furrowed at the top. The flesh is fragile, slightly elastic, with a faint odor and mild taste.

HABITAT: grows in spring from late March through May in cool, damp groves of elm, poplar, alder and hornbeam, often among Lesser Celandine, on clay and calcareous soils.

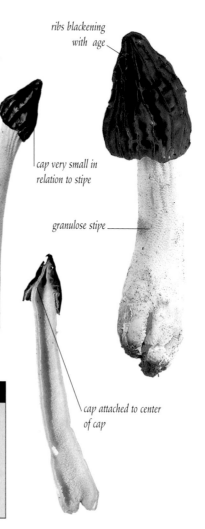

ribs blackening with age

cap very small in relation to stipe

granulose stipe

cap attached to center of cap

EDIBILITY/TOXICITY

Poisonous when raw, but good to eat when cooked. Only the cap tastes as good as a Morel, according to some experts. Because it is so small you need a lot of them to make a meal. Miniature Morels should be eaten right after picking, as it deteriorates quickly.

MORCHELLA ELATA

Tall Morel

DESCRIPTION: H:2³/₄-5 in (7-13 cm),
Ø: 1¹/₄-2 in (3-5 cm).
Conical cap, about twice as tall as it is
wide. The honeycombing is more or less
vertical, the cross-ribs being thinner than
the vertical ones. The cap is brownish-yellow to dark brown. Stem is short and
white, with a small circular depression
between the stipe and the cap.

HABITAT: Well-lit coniferous woods and
mixed woods, mainly in the mountains.
March and April, but sometimes as early as
from mid-February. Fairly uncommon.

cap more or less conical

stipe relatively thin

SPECIAL FEATURES

This Morel varies in shape depending on
the species of tree under which it grows.
and other environmental factors.
The Ribbed Morel *(Morchella costata)*
grows more frequently on detritus and
garbage heaps. The ribs are more vertical with cross-ribs at right angles to
them. It is often considered a mere
variety of *Morchella conica*.

MORCHELLA ESCULENTA

Morel

DESCRIPTION: The stipe and the cap are hollow and form a continuous cavity.

SPECIAL FEATURES

This fungus varies widely in shape. Some mycologists have divided it into several varieties or sub-species, but the white stem and honeycombed cap are very distinctive.

HABITAT: Very varied. Damp, cool deciduous woods, especially under ash, but also under poplar, willow and hazelnut. Also in hedgerows of these trees, in neglected apple orchards, old burnt patches, scrub, disturbed soil. April and May, until late June at high altitude. Fairly common, found in temperate zones throughout the world.

POTENTIAL CONFUSION

▶ *GYROMITRA ESCULENTA*
False Morel   DEADLY

EDIBILITY/TOXICITY

Poisonous when raw, but delicious when cooked. Morels are a valuable and expensive foodstuff, sold at gourmet foodstores. Fresh specimens are from the U.S. or imported from Europe and Turkey; dried Morels are imported from southeast Asia.

more or less globulose cap

stipe swollen at base

SPECIAL FEATURES

The Pale or Round Morel *(Morchella rotunda)* may grow larger. The cap is rounded, sometimes wider than it is tall. The honeycombing is also more rounded, with narrower ribs. The cap is straw-colored or pale ocher, and may be tinged with rust color on the ribs. The stipe is thicker and shorter but it has almost the same habitat as the Common Morel.

TUBER MELANOSPORUM

Black Truffle, Perigord Truffle

DESCRIPTION:
Ø:1¼-3¼ in (3-8 cm). Rounded, often irregular, lumpy shape, black covered with flattened pyramid-shaped warts. The flesh is firm and pale at first, then turning violet-black and heavily marbled with white veining which reddens when exposed to the air. The odor and taste are powerful and fragrant.

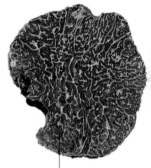

pyramid-shaped warts

Section of truffle

white marbling

HABITAT: grows underground a few inches below the surface, and may sometimes

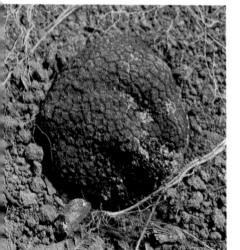

break through. Found in clearings in wooded areas, mainly under evergreen oaks on well-drained, calcareous soil. Found in southern France, Spain, Italy, and Portugal. Ripens from November through March. Rare, and has suffered from changes in the environment. Cultivated in evergreen oak or hazelnut plantations.

EDIBILITY

The Black Truffle is famous throughout the world for its delicious flavor. No other mushroom has such prestige or can match its powerful odor. The prices match the great demand and short supply, making it one of the most expensive foods in the world.

TUBER UNCINATUM
Burgundy Truffle

HABITAT: grows underground in woods of oak, hazelnut, beech, hornbeam, birch and pine. It is more of a woodland variety than the Black Truffle, growing on limestone soil, maturing from October through January. It is probably the most widely distributed and commonest truffle in continental Europe.

DESCRIPTION: Ø:³/₄-3¹/₄ in (2-8 cm).
The Burgundy Truffle is closely related to the Black or Perigord Truffle, but its warts are larger and the flesh is dark brown, also veined with white. It has a strong odor but not as aromatic as that of the Black Truffle and smells a little like ether.

SPECIAL FEATURES

Although the Burgundy Truffle is not particularly demanding as to temperature, it is more sensitive to rainfall. In order to flourish, it needs to have plenty of rain in July and August.

EDIBILITY

Very good to eat. The slightly unpleasant odor disappears during cooking. It has a better flavor than the Summer Truffle, though it has a lower status. It fetches high prices, nevertheless, costing around $200 a kilogram (2¼ lb). There are plans to grow this truffle in areas which are too cold for the Black Truffle.

THE PHRAGMOBASIDIOMYCETES

EXIDIA GLANDULOSA
Witches' Butter

DESCRIPTION: Ø:³/₄-2 in (2-5 cm).
A soft, black gelatinous mass, irregular,
sometimes lobed and sometimes globulose,
often folded and convoluted, growing alone
or in groups of two or three attached to
each other. Sometimes several individual
fruiting bodies mass together. The underside is covered with small conical papillae.
Grayish flesh, odorless and flavorless.

SPECIAL FEATURES

There is a more rounded form, *Exidia
truncata,* which is extremely common,
especially on oak branches and twigs.

HABITAT: on dead logs and branches of
deciduous trees. Present all year round, but
especially in winter. Common.

AURICULARIA MESENTERICA
Gray Brain Fungus

DESCRIPTION: Ø:up to 6 in (15 cm).
This crust-like fungus sometimes grows in a
ring of fruiting bodies. It is ¹/₈ to ¹/₄ in (0.3 to
0.5 cm) thick. The upper side is grayish with
concentric zones, some covered in gray
hairs, others folded and darker. The underside is gelatinous and convoluted; it is gray-
violet to purplish-brown in color. Flesh is
leathery and gelatinous.

SPECIAL FEATURES

Like the jelly funguses, the brain and ear
funguses are able to dry out and shrivel
during dry spells. When they reabsorb
water, they swell up again to resume
their normal shape.

HABITAT: on the dead wood of deciduous
trees, especially ash. Present all year round,
but especially in winter. Common.

AURICULARIA AURICULA JUDAE

Jew's Ear

DESCRIPTION: Ø:1½-4 in (4-10 cm). Cup-shaped, no stipe, irregular or in the shape of an ear. Interior surface is reddish-brown, smooth at first, then folding like the inside of an ear. The outer surface is velvety, reddish-brown, darkening with age, grayish-violet or grayish-olive. The flesh is gelatinous or elastic, almost translucent, coriaceous and shriveled when dry. No particular flavor or odor.

HABITAT: On the dead branches of deciduous trees, especially elder, sometimes on other deciduous trees, such as the walnut, and on the willow in damp places, such as

beside wide rivers. Grows in groups aligned vertically or horizontally on branches. Present all year round, especially winter and spring. Common to fairly uncommon, depending on climatic zone.

SPECIAL FEATURES

This is Mu-err, the "Cloud Ear" 'which the Chinese have been eating for centuries, mainly in its dried form, as an ingredient in many preparations or as a thickener for sauces.

Chinese medicine also claims therapeutic properties for this fungus. In order to meet the demand for it among oriental populations, the Jew's Ear is cultivated in China and elsewhere in southeast Asia, on logs of wood or, more recently, on artificial substrates. Most Europeans reject this fungus for eating, as they find it too insipid.

EDIBILITY

Quite good to eat, even raw, but slightly leathery.

TREMELLA MESENTERICA
Yellow Brain Fungus

DESCRIPTION: Ø:1¹/₄-3¹/₄ in (3-8 cm). Convoluted mass shaped like a brain, flaccid and gelatinous, trembling to the slightest touch. Generally sulfur yellow, but some specimens may be pale yellow or even white. The fungus becomes orange, tough, and brittle upon drying out.

HABITAT: on the dead branches of deciduous trees that have fallen on the ground. All year round. Common.

TREMELLODENDRON PALLIDUM
Pale Coral Fungus

DESCRIPTION: H:1¹/₄-4 in (3-10 cm), Ø:2-6 in (5-15 cm). Looks like a branching coral, with white or whitish vertical branches. Flesh gelatinous but tough.

HABITAT: grows on the ground in the deciduous or mixed forests of North America. Summer and fall.

THE PHRAGMOBASIDIOMYCETES

PSEUDOHYDNUM GELATINOSUM
Jelly Tongue

DESCRIPTION: H:1¹/₄-2¹/₂ in (3-6 cm), Ø: 1¹/₄-3¹/₄ in (3-8 cm). Spatulate or semicircular, very soft, gelatinous, and wobbly. Upper surface velvety, dirty white, gray-blue, turning brownish with age, and almost translucent. Underside covered in soft, gelatinous projections like blunt spines, white with bluish reflections. Stipe excentric, very short, and sometimes absent. The gelatinous flesh is almost translucent.

HABITAT: on rotting conifer stumps, often pine, sometimes buried in the ground. Fall and early winter. Fairly frequent, especially in the mountains. Does not grow outside the temperate zones.

EDIBILITY
Average. Sometimes tainted with a slight taste of resin. Can be eaten raw.

CALOCERA VISCOSA
Yellow Stagshorn Fungus

DESCRIPTION: H:1¹/₄-4 in (3-10 cm). The fungus is shaped like tiny stag's antlers or coral, ramified and viscid. the ramifications end in a point. The color is bright, golden to orange yellow, becoming darker as the fungus dries out. The flesh is rubbery.

HABITAT: firmly attached to the stumps and branches of the rotting wood of various species of conifer by a sort of whitish "root." All year round, but especially in late fall and early winter. Very common.

SPECIAL FEATURES
The stagshorn funguses are erect, sometimes branched fungi with tapering tops, reminiscent of the Clavaria. Their consistency may be gelatinous and elastic or leathery.

TOXICITY
Poisonous.

SERPULA LACRYMANS

Dry Rot

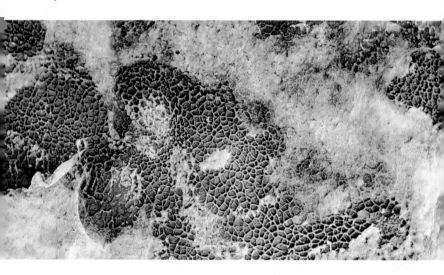

DESCRIPTION: Ø:up to 20 in (50 cm). The fungus takes a variety of forms depending on the stage of its development. The surface is velvety, olivaceous or rust brown, swollen and alveolate; the margin is velvety and white. The underside is covered with dirty yellow or brownish irregularly shaped, polygonal or labyrinthine pores, which release droplets of water at the edges (hence the epithet "lacrymans"). It has a pleasant smell when fresh, but becomes unpleasant as it ages.

HABITAT: under floorboards and carpets, in the walls, cupboards, cellars and damp unaired places. All year round.

SPECIAL FEATURES

This is the fearsome destroyer of older buildings, which eats away at the woodwork in damp constructions, especially those that are airless or uninhabited. Dry Rot requires a fairly damp atmosphere for it to take hold. It subsequently spreads by decomposing the wood and mortar, using the water in the materials and transporting it to the dry, inedible parts. It can thus thrive even in places which are not particularly damp, providing they remain airless and undisturbed. It is the scourge of stately homes and mansions.

THE APHYLLOPHORALES

SCHIZOPHYLLUM COMMUNE
Common Schizophyllum

DESCRIPTION: Ø:³/₄-2 in (2-5 cm).
A tiny fan-shaped or kidney-shaped fungus, from ¹/₁₆ to ¹/₆ in (2 to 4 mm) thick, and a very sinuous or lobed edge. The upper surface is whitish to grayish-beige and woolly. The underside has dark pink gills, radiating from a central point where it is attached to the substrate. These unusual gills are joined together in pairs and seem to be split lengthwise. The flesh has a faint odor and the flavor is mild.

HABITAT: the dead wood of any deciduous tree, rarer on conifers. All year round. Common from temperate regions to the equator.

PHLEBIA RADIATA
Many-capped Phlebia

DESCRIPTION: multiple fruiting bodies from 2 to 8 in (5 to 20 cm) in diameter. Irregular orange crust with darker, even violet, center, very veined and swollen, folded with a thick, fringed margin. The underside is pleated with radiating veins. Soft gelatinous flesh in young specimens. becoming leathery in the dry state.

HABITAT: on stumps or branches of deciduous trees (mainly birch and beech) more rarely on conifers. All year round, but less frequent in summer.

SPECIAL FEATURES

Trembling Rot *(Merulius tremellosus)*, which is also common, is very heavily folded on the underside, the folds resembling gills. It is soft and gelatinous and develops on the same wood as the Many-capped Phlebia.

HYMENOCHAETE TABACINA

Tobacco Brown Hymenochaete

DESCRIPTION: Ø:4-16 in (10-40 cm). A fungus that forms a leathery crust on wood, with small patches at first which spread and merge to form a large sheet. Velvety, tobacco or rust-brown surface, paler when the weather is dry. The sinuous margin is golden yellow then orange, turning brown with age. Leathery flesh.

HABITAT: on the dead wood of deciduous trees, mostly willows and hazel, whether standing or having fallen to the ground. Often localized at the edge of woods or in hedgerows. Present all year round. Common in temperate zones.

SPECIAL FEATURES

Mougeot's Hymenochaete de (*Hymenochaete mougeotii*), which is widely distributed throughout the world is easy to recognize due to its bright red color. It grows on dead branches of fir trees. *Hymenochaete rubiginosa* is a common species which grows on the trunks of old oak and chestnut trees. It forms little superimposed and imbricated caps of a leathery consistency, which are velvety in young specimens. The edge of the caps is reddish-brown, becoming darker with age.

CHONDROSTEREUM PURPUREUM
Silver-leaf Fungus

DESCRIPTION: Ø: ¼-2 in (0.5-5 cm).
This fungus may form a crust on wood or be attached to it at one side, leaving the edges of its cap free and undulating. The upper surface is white to reddish, hairy and with various parallel bands of color with a paler edge. The underside is smooth and slightly undulating. It is lilac-colored, turning brownish-violet with age. The flesh is thin, gelatinous at first, then coriaceous. It has no particular odor, and a mild flavor.

HABITAT: the individual fungi grow in large patches, one on top of the other, sometimes welded together, on the branches or trunks of lumber, mainly deciduous trees. Present all year round. Very common.

SPECIAL FEATURES

The Silver-leaf Fungus may also parasitize living but weakened trees. It causes Silver-leaf Disease in fruit trees.

STEREUM HIRSUTUM

Hairy Stereum

DESCRIPTION: Ø:³/₄-4 in (2-10 cm). Multiple imbricated or superimposed caps, barely ¹/₃₂ to ¹/₁₆ in (1 or 2 mm) thick, with an undulating or lobed margin. Velvety upper surface, colored in parallel yellow, orange, or reddish stripes which are much darker at the point where the fungus is attached to the substrate. Underside smooth and orange. Flesh coriaceous.

HABITAT: in dense colonies on dead or felled deciduous trees, from twigs to large branches, sometimes on pinewood. Present all year round. Very common.

STEREUM RUGOSUM

Rough Stereum

DESCRIPTION: Ø:³/₄-4 in (2-10 cm). Forms a crust ¹/₃₂ to ¹/₁₆ in (1 to 2 mm) thick, attached to wood on the upper surface, with a margin that is sometimes free. Upper surface (see below) grayish with a white edge. Underside white through ocher, smooth or bumpy, turning blood red when rubbed. The flesh is coriaceous, pale ocher in fresh young specimens, turning darker, and becoming tough and brittle during dry spells.

HABITAT: on the dead branches and trunks of deciduous trees, especially hazel and birch. Present all year round. Very common.

COLTRICIA PERENNIS

Persistent Coltricia

DESCRIPTION: Ø:³/₄-3¹/₄ in (2-8 cm). Funnel-shaped cap with thin, often undulating margin, sometimes incised or dentate. Several caps may be welded at the edges. The underside is velvety, covered in cinnamon or rust-colored concentric circles. The tiny pores on the underside of the cap are yellowish-white at first, then becoming coarser and turning brown, except at the edge, which stays white, as there are no pores there. Short, thick, central stipe (³/₄-2 in x ¹/₈-³/₈ in (2-5 cm x 0.3-0.7 cm)), wider at the base, velvety, paler at first, then blackening. Flesh, rust brown, thin and coriaceous.

HABITAT: grows on the ground in small groups, usually under conifers, in clearings or burnt, ground on sandy soil. Persists all year round, sometimes for several years on end. Common.

SPECIAL FEATURES

Fungi that form a crust on wood are said to be resupinate. Those attached to the growing medium on one side and grow one on top of the other are said to be dimidiate. Some, such as the Rough Stereum (*Stereum rugosum*), may appear in either of these forms.

PHAEOLUS SCHWEINITZII

Schweinitz's Polypore

DESCRIPTION: Ø:6-12 in (15-30 cm). Round or fan-shaped fungi, often imbricated or welded together, imprisoning twigs or plants within their growth. Upper surface hairy or downy, sulfur yellow with concentric circles of ocher, orange, or cinnamon, turning brown from the center. The margin stays yellow for a long time. The underside is labyrinthine, yellowish-green at first, turning reddish, and browning to the touch. The stipe is more or less developed, short and thick. Brown, tender, and fibrous flesh, with a slightly bitter flavor.

HABITAT: on the ground, growing in symbiosis (mycorrhiza) with the roots of living or dead conifers, pine, spruce, and larch. From early summer through late fall. Uncommon but widespread and found in many countries in the temperate zone.

THE APHYLLOPHORALES

HAPALOPILUS RUTILANS, PHAEOLUS RUTILANS
Reddening Hapalopilus

DESCRIPTION:
H:¹/₂-1¹/₂ in (1-4 cm),
Ø:2-4¹/₂ in (5-12 cm).
Fan-shaped or kidney-shaped
fungus, fixed to the substrate
over a large area, isolated or
in groups, specimens sometime welded together. The upper
side is of a uniform color, yellow-ocher through cinnamon,
velvety at first, then smooth.

The underside is russet and
covered in round, polygonal,
or elongated pores. Flesh soft
and spongy then corky, ocher
or cinnamon-colored.

HABITAT: dead branches of
deciduous trees, mainly oak,
beech, birch, chestnut, as well
as on conifers such as fir.
Spring through fall. Common.

PIPTOPORUS BETULINUS, UNGULINA BETULINA
Birch Polypore

DESCRIPTION:
Ø:4-10 in (10-25 cm).
Round or kidney-shaped cap,
³/₄ to 2¹/₂ in (2 to 6 cm) thick, stipe
absent, attached to the substrate by
a swelling. The upper surface is cof-
fee-colored, sometimes grayish, matte,
smooth, or velvety, cracking with age. The
margin is inrolled forming a ridge on the
pure white underside. which is covered with
rounded pores that are barely visible. The
flesh is white, soft and spongy, then corky.

SPECIAL FEATURES

This fungus has been put to various
uses, for example, to sharpen the cut-
throat razors once used by barbers.

EDIBILITY

Edible only in the young state, and not
very good to eat.

HABITAT: on the branches and trunks of
living or dead birch trees. Annual but may
persist for several years. Very common.

BJERKANDERA ADUSTA, POLYPORUS ADUSTUS, LEPTOPORUS ADUSTUS

Burnt Polypore

DESCRIPTION: Ø:1¹/₂-4 in (4-10 cm).
This fungus grows in tiers or imbricated clumps, in fan-shaped specimens or in a very thin layer only ¹/₄ in (6 mm) thick at the maximum. The upper side is gray-brown and velvety with a margin that is white at first, blackening with age. The underside is cinder gray, then turning darker gray, with tiny pores. The flesh is soft and elastic, then hard, whitish, and clearly sepa- rated from the pale gray tubes by a black line (seen in transverse section); fungal odor and slightly acid taste.

HABITAT: on stumps or on the dead or living trunks of deciduous trees, especially beech, more rarely on conifers. Present all year round, especially summer and fall. Very common.

DAEDALEOPSIS CONFRAGOSA, TRAMETES RUBESCENS

Blushing Bracket

DESCRIPTION: Ø:3¹/₄-6 in (8-15 cm).
Kidney-shaped cap, no thicker than 2 in (5 cm), and with a thin margin. Upper surface reddish, decorated with darker concentric cir- cles and sprinkled with little brown warts. Pores are dirty white, rounded and or slightly elongated, or forming a maze. They redden when touched, turning darker red with age.

HABITAT: on the dead and sometimes liv- ing branches of deciduous trees, and in damp places. Grows mainly on willow and elder, but also on popular, birch and hazel. Present all year round. Very common, rare at higher altitudes.

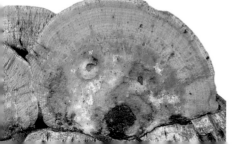

TRAMETES GIBBOSA
Bulbous Polypore

DESCRIPTION: H: $^3/_4$-2 in (2-5 cm), Ø: $3^1/_4$-8 in (8-20 cm).
Fan-shaped, sessile. Upper surface velvety, swollen at the point of fixation, white or cream, but very often greenish due to the growth of microscopic algae on the surface of the cap. There are a few concentric bands of color on the margin. The underside is creamy white, with large, elongated pores which may even take the form of short gills near the point of fixation. Flesh white and corky.

HABITAT: single or in tiered groups on branches and trunks of living or dead deciduous trees. Present all year round, and may persist for one or two years. Very common in the north, rarer in southern regions.

SPECIAL FEATURES

This fungus can grow to an impressive size, and is sometimes more than 3 ft (1 m) in diameter!

TRAMETES VERSICOLOR, CORIOLUS VERSICOLOR

Many-zoned Polypore

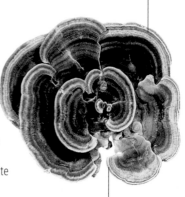

Parallel bands of various colors are what makes this fungus so easy to recognize.

Rosette formation

DESCRIPTION: Ø:1½-2 in (4-10 cm). Fan-shaped caps, tiered and bonded together, very thin with a very undulating margin. The range of colors includes white, gray, beige, black, blue-gray, and russet. These are arranged in parallel bands, but the margin is always paler, being white or pale yellow. Velvety patches alternate with smooth ones. The minute pores are white at first, turning yellow with age.

SPECIAL FEATURES

The fungus is used in Chinese medicine as a remedy against cancer of the liver and certain types of jaundice. In the West it is used as a decorative element in flower-arranging and on hats.

TRAMETES HIRSUTA

Hairy Tramete

DESCRIPTION: Ø:2-4½ in (5-12 cm). Fan-shaped fungus when growing on an upright medium, rosette-shaped when growing on a horizontal medium. Superior

face decorated with parallel bands of white, cream, ocher, or orange and covered with long, stiff hairs. Underside white, turning gray, with very small pores. Flesh white and elastic; faint odor and flavor.

HABITAT: on deciduous trees. All year round. Fairly common in many countries.

SPECIAL FEATURES

In the Trametes polypores, there is no separation between flesh and tubes, because the tubes are hollowed out of the flesh.

LENZITES BETULINA

Birch Lenzite

Upper surface

DESCRIPTION: large:2-4 in (5-10 cm). Thin (¾ in (2 cm) maximum), fan-shaped cap, often imbricated . Upper surface hirsute and velvety, covered in white, gray, or ocher concentric parallel bands, often colonized by algae which give it a greenish color. There are pale gray or ocher crowded gills on the underside, some of which are forked. The flesh is pale, coriaceous, elastic, or corky.

HABITAT: on various living or dead

deciduous trees—not confined to birch—and felled logs, in cool places. All year round. Quite common and found in many countries.

underside

FOMES FOMENTARIUS
Hoof Fungus; Tinder Fungus

DESCRIPTION: H:1½-8 in (4-20 cm), Ø:4-16 in (10-40 cm).
The upper surface is ocher or reddish-brown,

turning gray with semi-circular stripes or folds. The underside is cream to gray-brown with tiny pores which darken when touched. The reddish-brown flesh is as hard as wood.

SPECIAL FEATURES

This fungus probably played an important role in the life of prehistoric man, as it was certainly used as a way of preserving and transporting fire, since it burns very slowly.

HABITAT: on the trunks of living or dead deciduous trees, especially beech and birch. All year round. Fairly common.

FISTULINA HEPATICA
Beefsteak Fungus

DESCRIPTION: Ø:4-10 in (10-25 cm).
The fungus is elongated like a tongue or semi-circular, It sometimes has a short stipe by which it is attached to the wood. The upper surface is brick red, sticky, and densely covered with little papillae. The pores on the underside are cream at first, then reddish-pink, staining darker red when touched. The flesh is soft and spongy, red with paler patches, and oozing a red juice when cut. The tubes are not bonded together and are easily separable. Acidic taste.

HABITAT: at the base of living oaks or chestnuts. Late summer and fall. Common in certain places and found in many countries in the temperate zone.

EDIBILITY
Good to eat when young.

THE APHYLLOPHORALES

GANODERMA APLANATUM, G. LIPSIENSE
Artist's Fungus

DESCRIPTION:
Ø:4-16 in (10-40 cm).
The fungus is fan-shaped or semi-circular and is attached to the substrate over a large area on one side. It is quite thin (³/₄ to 3¹/₄ in (2 to 8 cm)). The upper surface is knobbly, and furrowed, ocher-brown or cinnamon with a very thin, white margin. When the spores are ejected, the surface is covered with a powdery, ocher layer. The underside is white, turning russet, and browning to the touch. The flesh is corky, brown with some white streaks.

HABITAT: on stumps and dead or living tree trunks of deciduous trees or more rarely on conifers. Persists for several years. Common and found in many countries.

GANODERMA LUCIDUM
Lacquered Bracket

DESCRIPTION: 2-12 in (5-30 cm), Ø:2-8 in (5-20 cm).
Circular or kidney-shaped cap. Upper surface reddish-brown, knobbly, and hard with a brilliant glaze. Margin yellow-orange in young specimens. Underside white, turning brown. Shiny stipe lateral or excentric, vertical, fairly twisted, and the same color or darker than the cap. Flesh elastic but coriaceous. Not edible.

SPECIAL FEATURES

The fungus is highly prized in Chinese medicine, and is used to cure a number of infections and illnesses.

HABITAT: on stumps and dead trunks of deciduous trees, sometimes on buried roots. Summer and fall. Uncommon.

TRICHAPTUM ABIETINUM, HIRSCHIOPORUS ABIETINUS
Fir Bracket Fungus

DESCRIPTION:
Ø:¹/₂-1¹/₄ in (1-3 cm). Flattish bracket fungi with imbricated on bonded caps, often in rows. The upper surface is gray-brown, hairy, sometimes greenish due to the growth of algae, and violet or purple on the margin. The underside has small, violet, rounded, or angular pores of uneven size, in a labyrinthine pattern, which turn brown with age. Flesh thin and coriaceous.

HABITAT: on the trunks of dead or felled conifers, sometimes on living trees. Grows from sea level to the tree line. Present all year round. Common in temperate zones.

POLYPORUS LEPTOCEPHALUS, P. VARIUS
Variable Bracket Fungus

DESCRIPTION: H:1¹/₄-2³/₄ in (3-7 cm), Ø: 2-4 in (5-10 cm).

Irregular, circular, or fan-shaped bracket, sometimes lobed, or with a sinuous margin, hollow at the stipe end, yellow ocher or reddish, with fine, darker radial striations. Underside white then browning, tubes more or less decurrent, very small pores. Excentric or central stipe, tapering at the typically black base. Whitish or yellowish flesh; pleasant odor and mild flavor.

HABITAT: on dead wood and stumps of deciduous trees, sometimes on living trees. From spring to late fall. Common and found all over the temperate zones.

POLYPORUS SQUAMOSUS, MELANOPUS SQUAMOSUS

Dryad's Saddle

DESCRIPTION: H:2-4 in (5-10 cm), Ø:4-20 in (10-50 cm). Kidney-shaped or circular cap, straw to ocher in color, covered with large reddish or brown scales. Underside whitish, with decurrent tubes and large pores, from $^1/_{32}$ to $^1/_8$ in (1 to 3 mm). Very short, thick stipe (up to $3^1/_4$ in (8 cm) long and 2 in (5 cm) wide), lateral or excentric, rarely central, white except at the base, where it is black. Firm white flesh. Flavor and odor of flour.

HABITAT: grows in tiers on stumps or at the base of the trunks of deciduous trees, such as willow, poplar, walnut, and maple, in well-lit woods, parks, roadsides, and beside Spring through fall. Fairly common.

EDIBILITY

Poor quality, but edible when young.

POLYPORUS DURUS, P. BADIUS, P. PICIPES

Bay Polypore

DESCRIPTION: resembles *P. leptocephalus,* but larger. The surface of the cap is very shiny and pale at first, later becoming dark brown, with a paler border.

HABITAT: on dead wood and deciduous tree-stumps, often in groups of two or three. Spring through fall. Fairly common.

MERIPILUS GIGANTEUS, POLYPORUS GIGANTEUS

Giant Polypore

DESCRIPTION: Ø:2-16 in (10- 40 cm).
Cap forming voluminous, large, thin, fan-shaped tufts, with a sinuous, lobed margin. Surface rough, ocher, reddish or dark brown. Pores whitish, blackening to the touch and on maturity. Stipes bonded together at the base into a single point of attachment to the substrate. Flesh soon becomes coriaceous, white, turning pink then black when cut. Strongly fungal but pleasant odor and slightly acid flavor.

HABITAT: on stumps or at the base of deciduous trees. Late summer through early fall. Fairly common.

SPECIAL FEATURES

Some clumps are of gigantic proportions. They may weigh several dozen pounds and can measure up to 40 in (1 m) in diameter.

FOMITOPSIS PINICOLA, UNGULINA MARGINATA

Marginate Polypore

DESCRIPTION: H:1¼-4 in (3-10 cm), Ø:4-16 in (10-40 cm).
Fan-shaped fungus without a stipe. The upper surface has a resinous crust of paler yellow turning reddish brown, and finally gray-black. Thick, yellow-orange margin. Underside whitish or cream, secreting large drops of color-less liquid at the margin while the fungus is growing.

HABITAT: mainly on stumps and logs of dead or living conifers. Present all year round, perennial. Common in places and in many countries.

THE APHYLLOPHORALES

INONOTUS HISPIDUS
Shaggy Polypore

DESCRIPTION: Ø:3$\frac{1}{4}$-12 in (8-30 cm).
Fan-shaped cap, up to 4 in (10 cm) thick at
the base. Grows singly or in tufts. Cap reddish, turning brown outward from the point
of attachment. The surface is thickly covered
with stiff hairs. The pores are orange-red,
then brown. The flesh is soft at first and yellow then coriaceous and rust-colored. Pleasant odor and mild flavor.

HABITAT: on living deciduous trees, where
they have been damaged, or on old trees,
including apple, pear, aspen, and mountain-
ash. Summer through fall; it disappears
when the weather turns cold, but reappears
annually. Fairly common and widespread.

SCHIZOPORA PARADOXA, IRPEX PARADOXA, PORIA VERSIPORA
Variable Schizopore

DESCRIPTION: L:2-12 in (5-30 cm), thick-
ness:$\frac{1}{8}$-$\frac{1}{4}$ in (0.3-0.5 cm).
White to cream patches, dispersed at first
but growing together to form a large sheet.
Short tubes at the margin, lengthening
toward the center and looking like spines
with age. Tiny white pores, stained with
ocher, varying in shape from circular, elongated, angular, or labyrinthine, absent on
the margin. Flesh $\frac{1}{8}$ in (1 mm) thick, whitish,
leathery, toughening when dry.

HABITAT: on deciduous trees, especially
hornbeam, ash, and oak, in forests and
parks. Present all year round. Common and
widespread throughout the temperate zone.

PLICATUROPSIS CRISPA
Shriveled Polypore

DESCRIPTION: L:$^1/_2$-$^3/_4$ in (1-2 cm).
The little fan-shaped caps are borne on a very short stem. The upper surface, is velvety and varies from yellow through fawn, some-times with alternate bands, paler at the margin, often undulating and turned under at the edge. The underside has radial whitish folds which look like shriveled gills. The flesh is soft and elastic when fresh, hard and brittle in dry weather. The fungus is odorless and has a mild flavor.

HABITAT: grows in large numbers on the dead branches of various deciduous trees, especially beech and hazel. Summer and fall. Fairly common but easily passes unnoticed.

THELEPHORA TERRESTRIS
Earth-fan

DESCRIPTION: Ø:2-4 in (5-10 cm).
The fungus actually consists of numerous individual fruiting-bodies bonded together at the base and of unequal size, tiered, spread out, or funnel-shaped. The marge is fringed. Twigs and pine-needles are often encrusted in the flesh. The upper surface is reddish-brown then paler at the edge and covered in stiff hairs. The underside is paler, irregularly warty or wrinkled. The flesh is coriaceous and spongy.

HABITAT: on the ground, on pine-needles, or half-buried twigs, in coniferous or mixed forests. Dry, acid soil. All year round but mainly in the fall. Fairly common.

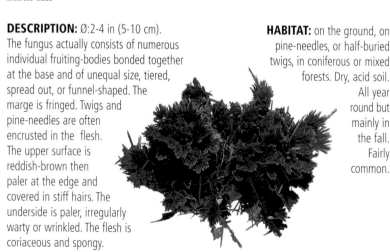

SCUTIGER OVINUS, ALBATRELLUS OVINUS, CALOPORUS OVINUS

Sheep Polypore

DESCRIPTION: H: 1½-2 in (4-10 cm), Ø: 2¾-6 in (7-15 cm).
Cap has a thin margin, sometimes lobed, white at first then yellowing and cracking, turning reddish when old. Small round pores of the same color. Short, thick, central or excentric stipe, similar in color to the cap. Flesh pale with mild flavor.

HABITAT: in groups, with stipes or caps sometimes welded together, on moss in old forests. From late summer through late fall. Fairly common in mountainous regions, rare in the lowlands.

EDIBILITY

Good to eat when young, but often worm-eaten, with firm flesh becoming coriaceous and bitter with age.

SPECIAL FEATURES

This fungus bears some resemblance to the common Hedgehog Fungus, but the sheep polypore has no spines.

HYDNUM REPANDUM

Hedgehog Mushroom, Wood Hedgehog

DESCRIPTION: H:2-4 in (5-10 cm), Ø:1¼-6 in (3-15 cm).
The irregularly shaped undulating cap is sometimes lobed and bonded to other caps. The margin is inrolled in young specimens. It is creamy white, slightly velvety, and reddens slightly. The underside of the cap is covered in soft spines the same color as the cap which are easily detached. They are ½ in (1 cm) long in older specimens. Stipe central or excentric, short and up to 1¼ in (3 cm) thick fleshy and full, irregular, often curved and swollen at the base, deeply embedded in the soil and the same color as the cap but reddening when handled. Flesh firm and brittle, white, becoming orange-red when exposed to the air for a few hours. Flavor mild or slightly peppery, slightly bitter in older specimens. Often grows alongside the Reddening Hedgehog Mushroom (*Hydnum rufescens*).

SPECIAL FEATURES

The Reddening Hedgehog Mushroom (*Hydnum rufescens*) is sometimes confused with the Hedgehog Fungus, but the stipe is central and thinner and the fungus is smaller and redder. Both mushrooms are edible.

THE APHYLLOPHORALES

HABITAT: forms rings in the moss of forests of oak, beech, or chestnut, mixed forests, and coniferous forests in fall and early winter. Its fleshy consistency enables it to resist minor frosts.

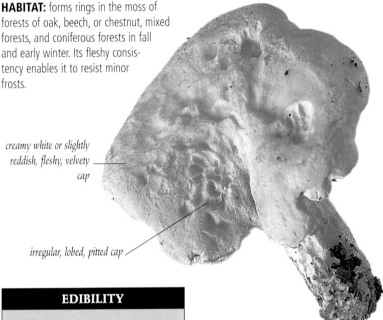

creamy white or slightly reddish, fleshy, velvety cap

irregular, lobed, pitted cap

EDIBILITY

Although some people find it to be of little interest, the Hedgehog Mushroom is often considered good to eat. The firm, crunchy flesh has a slightly spicy taste, reminiscent of that of the Chanterelle. The Hedgehog Mushroom should be eaten young, because it becomes bitter as it ages. To remove any bitterness, it is advisable to throw away any liquid given off by the mushroom at the start of cooking, instead of letting it evaporate. It should be simmered over low heat. The firm flesh makes it possible to pickle small specimens in vinegar and serve them as condiments.

SPECIAL FEATURES

The Hedgehog Mushroom is too distinctive to be confused with any poisonous variety, since none of the mushrooms with spines in place of gills are poisonous. Seen from above, the Sheep Polypore *(Albatrellus ovinus),* which is good to eat, looks very much like the Hedgehog Fungus, but it has pores instead of spines on the underside of the cap and is more likely to be worm-eaten.

AURISCALPIUM VULGARE
Ear-pick Fungus

DESCRIPTION: H:1¹/₄-4 in (3-10 cm), Ø:¹/₂-³/₄ in (1-2 cm).
The cap is kidney-shaped, brown or reddish-brown, covered in fine, dense hairs. The spines are long and large in relation to the size of the cap, and are dirty white, then turning brown. The stipe is thin, lateral, darker than the cap and also hairy. The flesh is very thin, coriaceous, and white. The species is easily identifiable due to it being the only variety of hedgehog fungus to grow on pine-cones.

HABITAT: mostly grows on pine-cones which are half-buried in the soil. All year round, especially in spring and fall. Common, but difficult to spot due to its size and color. Inedible.

SPECIAL FEATURES

All fungi with spines instead of gills were once included in the genus *Hydnum* and the Ear-pick Fungus had the botanical name of *Hydnum auriscalpium*. Today the genus has been split into a dozen different genera based on ecological differences and microscopic characteristics. These fungi have even been placed in different families.

HERICIUM RAMOSUM, H. CLATHROIDES

White Coral Fungus

DESCRIPTION: H:3¼-6 in (8-15 cm), Ø:4-10 in (10-25 cm).

Ivory white or cream, yellowing with age. The fungus is attached to the substrate by a thick stipe, which branches into fruiting-bodies to which the spines are attached. The spines are arranged in rows on the sides or underside. The flesh is fragile and very friable, white, with a faint and pleasant odor, and mild flavor.

HABITAT: grows at the base of dead deciduous trees, especially beech. Late summer and fall. Uncommon and rather localized.

SPECIAL FEATURES

The Coral Fungus *(Hericium coralloides)*, a related species, grows on confers; the spines are of various lengths and are generally ramified and are found at the end of branches only.

EDIBILITY

Good to eat when young, becoming slightly coriaceous and bitter with age.

CRATERELLUS CORNUCOPIOIDES

Horn of Plenty

DESCRIPTION: H:1$\frac{1}{2}$-4$\frac{1}{2}$ in (4-12 cm), Ø: 1$\frac{1}{4}$-3$\frac{1}{4}$ in (3-8 cm).
Trumpet-shaped fungus whose margin is curved outward and becomes brown, streaked with darker lines which turn black in damp weather. The exterior surface is gray, pruinose, smooth, or slightly veined, then rough or swollen, and also black when wet. The stipe is sometimes sinuous, becoming thinner at the base and irregularly swollen. The flesh is thin and elastic, the flavor mild and the odor fruity. The flesh is never worm-eaten.

HABITAT: in very large colonies in lowland forests of oak, hornbeam, and hazelnut. Rarer on high ground under conifers. Prefers very damp soil, clay, limestone, or neutral

SPECIAL FEATURES

Two other smaller, rarer species of Craterellus are closely related to the Horn of Plenty which the French call the Trumpet of the Dead, no doubt due to its black color. They are:
- the Sinuous Chanterelle *(Pseudocraterellus sinuosus)*, which is paler in color, ocher-brown or gray, and decorated with brown fibrils and with a very sinuous, lobed margin. The external surface of the trumpet is ochraceous and also covered in a white bloom. It grows in the same type of forests, but on more acid soils.
- the Gray Chanterelle *(Pseudocraterellus cinereus)* has a strong odor of mirabelle plum and by the presence of strongly marked, gill-like folds below the cap. It grows in the same habitat as the Horn of Plenty.

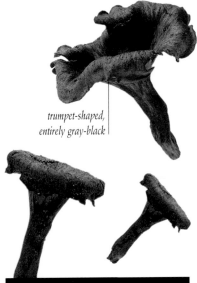

trumpet-shaped, entirely gray-black

(non-acidic). From late September through late November, occasionally appearing in June if there is enough rain, but such growth is very localized and short-lived.
The fungus seems to grow in cycles, which would explain why it is abundant in certain years and absent in others. However, it may be abundant or rare in the same season, depending on the region.

EDIBILITY

The Horn of Plenty makes excellent eating. It can be stewed and made into a sauce to be eaten with venison, jugged hare, and other types of game. It is also added to stews, pâtés, and other types of charcuterie. These trumpet-shaped fungi have the advantage of drying easily and the flavor is even enhanced by dessication. Once dried, it can even be crushed to powder and used as a condiment, to flavor sauces. Before cleaning the fungus, it should be split lengthwise because the hollow interior often contains earth, insect larvae, and even slugs.

CANTHARELLUS CIBARIUS
Chanterelle

DESCRIPTION: H: 1¼-4½ in (3-12 cm), Ø: 1¼-4 in (3-10 cm).

The whole fungus is entirely bright yellow. The cap is convex at first, with an inrolled, regular margin. It later sinks into a funnel-shape, and the margin becomes more sinuous and undulating. The folds or veins under the cap look like gills. They are thick and decurrent, straight at first, then forked and then more sinuous and more heavily forked.

EDIBILITY

A very delicious mushroom, highly sought after and sold commercially in many countries. It is never worm-eaten and is easy to store and preserve. The Chanterelle should be simmered over low heat. It is used as an accompaniment to poultry, fish, or game and can even be eaten raw.

Whole fungus completely egg-yellow

thick, forked ribs

With transverse, interconnecting veins. The stipe tapers slightly toward the base. The whitish flesh becomes more fibrous in the stipe and with age. The flavor is mild and slightly peppery. and the pleasant fruity odor is often compared to apricot or plum.

HABITAT: Grows in groups in forests, groves, or plantations of deciduous trees, principally oak, hazel, or chestnut, as well as under conifers. Appears in late May through October on acidic soil. The Chanterelle appears in the same places every year after heavy rain followed by several days of warm weather. It is common in many regions, but is tending to become rarer, especially in Eastern Europe.

There are several varieties or forms of the Chanterelle. When it grows under hazelnut, it is smaller, less fleshy, and appears later in the year. When it grows under beech and fir, it is more fleshy and much paler.

The *amethysteus* variety can be found in the undergrowth under deciduous trees. It is quote large (Ø: 2-4½ in (5-12 cm)), and has violet scales in the center of the cap.

The *bicolor* variety, which is also found under deciduous trees, is very pale yellow beneath the cap. The other parts are identical to the classic form.

Cantharellus friesii, is only ½ to 1½ in (1 to 4 cm) in diameter and is brighter orange.

POTENTIAL CONFUSION

▶ *OMPHALOTUS OLEARIUS*
Olive tree Pleurotus   POISONOUS

▶ *HYGROPHOROPSIS AURANTIACA*
False Chanterelle   POISONOUS

CANTHARELLUS LUTESCENS

Yellowing Chanterelle

underside of cap yellow or salmon-colored

very long, orange yellow stipe

pressed, and may have a central furrow. It is bright yellow, even when old. Very thin flesh smelling of plum.

DESCRIPTION: H: 2-4½ in (5-12 cm), Ø: 1¼-2½ in (3-6 cm).

The thin cap funnel-shaped cap is often pierced in the center. The margin is often curved downward, but later flattens and becomes undulating, curly, and sometimes lobed. The surface is covered in brown fibrils on a yellowish-brown background. The underside of the cap is lightly creased and brightly colored orange or salmon pink. which contrasts with the brown upper surface. The stipe is long and thin, up to 4½ in (12 cm) long for a diameter of less than ½ in (1 cm). It is cylindrical or very often slightly com-

HABITAT: deciduous or coniferous forests, especially under pines, from the lowlands to the mountains, on acidic soil. Absent from certain regions, but very common in others. Grows in large colonies. Fall and early winter. In warmer climates, such as the South of France, it grows in winter (until February).

EDIBILITY

Although the flesh is very thin, the Yellowing Chanterelle makes particularly good eating. It is often confused with the Tubular Chanterelle and both fungi are called the Gray Chanterelle, but the flavor is much stronger and the consistency less rubbery. It can also be dried very easily. All Chanterelles can be identified by the ribs or veins on the underside of the cap, instead of gills.

CANTHARELLUS TUBAEFORMIS
Tubular Chanterelle

DESCRIPTION: H: 2-4½ in (5-12 cm), Ø: ¾-2¾ in (2-7 cm).

When young, the fungus is nail-shaped, with a tiny cap on a long, narrow stipe. The cap expands gradually and becomes concave, eventually becoming deeply funnel-shaped. The center of the cap is often pierced with a small hole which leads to the hollow stipe. The margin is inrolled in the young specimen, becoming sinuous and undulating. The upper surface of the cap is ocher through

EDIBILITY

Quite good to eat, though not strongly flavored, and of a rather rubbery consistency. It is never worm-eaten and grows in large colonies, so a basket is soon filled. It can thus be prepared like a vegetable. It dries very well, as long as it is not waterlogged when picked, a condition that should be avoided when picking any mushroom.

gray-brown and the underside is covered thick, widely spaced, decurrent, forked folds or veins instead of gills. These are yellow, then turning gray or grayish-violet. The stipe is very long in relation to the cap, often compressed and hollow. It is golden, then ocher and finally grayish like the folds

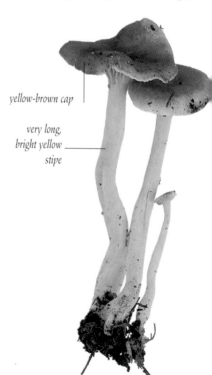

thick, decurrent folds, resembling the gills of the agarics, yellow then gray

SPECIAL FEATURES

The Tubular Chanterelle is sometimes confused with other types of Chanterelle but this is not important because all of them are edible. However, there is a danger that some small varieties of Cortinarius, such as the Cinnamon Cortinarius *(Cortinarius cinnamomeus)* may grow in the midst of a colony of Chanterelles and may accidentally be picked along with them. The Cinnamon Cortinarius does not have a funnel-shaped cap and it has true gills which are not decurrent. It is therefore very important to sort the harvest carefully.

There is a yellow form of the Tubular Chanterelle, which is golden-yellow all over and has a smaller cap with a diameter of no more than 1¼ in (3 cm). In this variety, the margin unrolls very late and the flesh is thicker. The variety is commoner under deciduous trees than it is under conifers.

yellow-brown cap

very long, bright yellow stipe

at the top. The flesh is thin, rather elastic, with a faint odor and mild flavor.

HABITAT: grows in colonies, consisting of tightly packed specimens, on moss or pine-needle litter in coniferous forests, mainly under Scots pine and spruce, more rarely under deciduous trees. It often hides under heaps of lopped branches or beside such heaps, as well as near old, rotten stumps. It normally appears in fall and early winter. but it is not uncommon to find it growing in mid-winter. The winter specimens usually remain small. The fungus persists well into the cold weather and can withstand a certain amount of frost. The fungus freezes but thaws out when the weather turns warmer.

GOMPHUS FLOCCOSUS
Scaly Gomphus

DESCRIPTION: H:2³/₄-7 in (7-18 cm), Ø:2-6 in (5-15 cm).
The fungus is cylindrical at first, expanding at the top and funnel-shaped and hollow at the bottom. The yellow to orange-red margin is undulating and lobed and covered in scales that are flat at the margin and erect in the center. The cream, yellow, or ocher

EDIBILITY
Although occasionally eaten, this fungus and its relatives should be avoided, since they are indigestible and sometimes bitter.

outer surface is wrinkled and folded. The stipe is thick and tapering at the bottom, becoming hollow, smooth or fibrillose, yellow to orange. The flesh is whitish.
HABITAT: under conifers or in mixed forests in summer. Quite common.

CLAVARIA FRAGILIS, C. VERMICULARIS
Fragile Fairy Club

DESCRIPTION: H:1¹/₂-4 in (4-10 cm), Ø:¹/₁₆-¹/₆ in (0.2- 0.4 cm).
This fungus often grows in tufts, and it may be upright, cylindrical, or spindle-shaped, becoming slightly compressed or with a vertical furrow, often twisted, hollow, and brittle, with a pointed or rounded top. It is pure white, yellowing with age at the tip. The flesh is odorless.

HABITAT: in grass or on bare soil. Spring through fall. Uncommon but widespread.

THE APHYLLOPHORALES

CLAVULINA CINEREA
Ash-gray Fairy Club

DESCRIPTION: H: 1¼-4 in (3-10 cm).
The fungus looks like a tiny bunch of antlers with flattened, curved, twisting branches. the tips are tapering and rounded, and of uneven lengths. They are ash gray, sometimes tinged with lilac. The stem is about ½ in (1 cm) in diameter. The soft flesh is slightly bitter and odorless.

HABITAT: beneath deciduous trees, on the ground, more rarely under conifers, often in colonies. Fall. Fairly common.

CLAVULINA CRISTATA
Crested Fairy Club

DESCRIPTION:
H: 1¼-4 in (3-10 cm).
This Fairy Club is shaped like a bush or, when the branches are tightly packed, like a cauliflower. It is usually pure white, but sometimes it is pale gray. The tips of the branches are flattened and dentate or lobed like a coxcomb. The flesh is white, odorless, and mild.

HABITAT: On bare soil or decomposing wood, along paths, in ruts, and under deciduous and coniferous trees. Summer to early winter. Very common.

EDIBILITY

Some people eat this Fairy Club and consider it to have a pleasant flavor, but it is not for all tastes.

RAMARIA ARAIOSPORA
Fiery Coral Fungus

DESCRIPTION: H: 2-4¹/₂ in (5-12 cm), Ø: 1¹/₄-2³/₄ in (3-7 cm).
This Coral Fungus is thickly branched above the base, and bright red or scarlet, the tips becoming orange to yellow. The base is white or yellowish-white. The stipe is very short or absent, 1¹/₄ in (3 cm) long at the most. The flesh is thick and fibrous.

HABITAT: grows in the fall under western hemlock (*Tsuga heterophylla),* in North America.

EDIBILITY
Good to eat, and harvested in large quantities in the northwestern United States.

POTENTIAL CONFUSION
▶ *RAMARIA FORMOSA*   Beautiful Coral Fungus   POISONOUS

RAMARIA FLACCIDA
Flaccid Coral Fungus

DESCRIPTION:: H: 1¹/₄-2¹/₂ in (3-6 cm).
Yellow ocher to brownish ocher branches ¹/₈ to ¹/₄ in (1 to 3 mm) thick. Color does not change when touched. Branches end in one or two paler teeth. Stipe ¹/₄ to ¹/₂ in (0.5 to 1 cm) thick with white base. White, fibrous flesh, bitter taste.

HABITAT: grows on the ground in lines or circles, under conifers, especially Norway spruce, in mountainous regions at altitude. Summer and fall. Common.

THE APHYLLOPHORALES

RAMARIA FORMOSA
Beautiful Coral Fungus

DESCRIPTION:
H: 4-12 in (10-30 cm), Ø:2-8 in (5-20 cm). This handsome coral fungus has erect, cylindrical branches, which may be straight or bent and have short ramifications at the tips. It is an attractive salmon pink, except at the tips which are brilliant lemon yellow. As it grows older, the fungus becomes ochraceous orange all over. The stipe is short, whitish then turning pinkish. The pinkish-gray flesh is brittle when cut. The flavor is fairly bitter.

HABITAT: deciduous forests, especially under beech, also found in mixed woods. Summer through fall. Uncommon.

TOXICITY
Strongly purgative, causing persistent diarrhea.

RAMARIA STRICTA
Erect Coral Fungus

DESCRIPTION: H: 1½-4 in (4-10 cm). This coral fungus has vertical, densely packed, straight and vee-shaped branches. In young specimens the color varies from the narrow, pointed tip which is pale yellow and the lower part of the branches which is reddish ocher or pinkish ocher. The whole fungus reddens with age and turns brown when rubbed. It has no stipe; the lower part forms a short trunk which extends into the white filaments of the mycelium embedded in the substrate. The flesh is white or pale yellow, coriaceous, with a pleasant odor but bitter, peppery taste.

HABITAT: on the dead and rotten branches of deciduous trees (especially beech) or on conifers, sometimes embedded in the soil. Also found on sawdust or wood shavings. Summer through fall. Fairly common.

RAMARIOPSIS KUNZEI, CLAVARIA KUNZEI

Kunze's Coral Fungus

DESCRIPTION: H: 1$\frac{1}{2}$-4 in (4-10 cm), Ø: 1$\frac{1}{4}$-2$\frac{3}{4}$ in (3-7 cm).

This bushy coral fungus has few but dense ramifications, ending in short forks. The stipe is absent or only $\frac{1}{2}$ to $\frac{3}{4}$ in (1 to 2 cm) long and $\frac{1}{6}$ in (4 mm) wide Fragile flesh.

HABITAT: on the ground or more rarely on rotting wood, in woodland, meadows, or at the edge of fields. Summer through fall. Uncommon.

SPARASSIS CRISPA

Cauliflower Fungus

DESCRIPTION:

Ø:4-16 in (10-40 cm).

A globulose mass of densely packed, wrinkled fronts, looking like a cauliflower or a sponge, creamy white at first, then yellow ocher. The branches are flattened and sinuous, divided and very numerous, splitting at tips when old. Very short thick, white stipe. Flesh smelling slightly of cinnamon, tender but slightly coriaceous when older, tasting of hazelnut.

HABITAT: Almost always on or near conifer stumps or living trunks, especially pine, sometimes spruce. Often grows again in the

same places. Fall, sometimes summer. Fairly common in mountainous regions.

POTENTIAL CONFUSION

▶ *RAMARIA FORMOSA*
Beautiful Coral Fungus   POISONOUS

EDIBILITY

Good to eat when young. Flavor of older specimens less pleasant, and becoming rubbery and slightly laxative. It is often cooked with cream and good seasoning. It needs long and careful washing.

SPECIAL FEATURES

Some specimens of the Cauliflower Fungus can weigh up to 22 lb (10 kg)! A very similar but much rarer species, the Leafy Fungus *(Sparassis brevipes)*, is only found near or at the base of oak trees. The branches are flatter, wider and floppier. It smells slightly of bleach and is said to be slightly toxic.

CLAVARIADELPHUS PISTILARIS

Giant Fairy Club

DESCRIPTION:
H: 4-10 in (10-25 cm),
Ø: ³/₄-2 in (2-5 cm).
This club-shaped fungus
can take on very diverse
appearances. It may be tall
or short, with a swollen
rounded tip, or rather puffy
and bloated. The surface
is smooth at first, becoming deeply wrinkled or
folded. Yellow at first,
reddening when mature.
The flesh is soft in young
specimens, later becom-
ing hard and fibrous. It is
white, changing to red-
dish-brown when cut.
Faint odor, bitter taste.

HABITAT: singly or in
groups under deciduous
trees, especially beech, on
limestone soil. Late summer
through fall. Uncommon.

SPECIAL FEATURES

The Truncated Fairy Club *(Clavariadel-
phus truncatus)* looks very similar, but
the top is not rounded, but flat, as if
truncated.

EDIBILITY

Not good to eat due to the bitter flavor
and fibrous texture. In some places,
notably eastern Europe, it is picked
young, then pickled in vinegar
and used as a condiment.

THE APHYLLOPHORALES

CLAVARIADELPHUS TRUNCATUS
Truncated Fairy Club

DESCRIPTION: H: 3¼-6 in (8-15 cm), Ø: ¾-1½ in (2-4 cm).
This fungus is shaped like an upturned cone,. The top is swollen and the margin extends over the edge, forming a ridge. It is pale yellow, turning ocher and finally reddish. Stipe indistinct. The lower part is ocher and slightly wrinkled. The flesh is firm, soon becoming spongy, white or pale ocher, with a faint odor and sweet taste.

HABITAT: forests of fir and mixed forests in the mountains, on limestone soil and in cool, humid regions. Late summer and fall. Fairly uncommon.

EDIBILITY
Edible, but of little interest.

CLAVULINOPSIS HELVOLA
Yellow Fairy Club

DESCRIPTION: H:1¼-2½ in (3-6 cm).
Tall narrow, rounded spikes or club-shaped fungus without branches, often bent or curved, and may have a vertical furrow. Golden-yellow, paler toward the base. Flesh, pale yellow and fibrous. Odorless but with a mild flavor.

HABITAT: isolated or in groups, in the grass or moss of lawns or in woods. Fall. Widespread but uncommon.

THE TRICHOLOMATALES

CUPHOPHYLLUS PRATENSIS, CAMAROPHYLLUS PRATENSIS
Meadow Wax-cap

cream-colored gills, wide apart, slightly decurrent. Thick stipe narrowing toward the base and often curved, smooth and brittle, paler in color than the cap. Flesh thick in the center of the cap, pale orange. Pleasant odor and mild flavor.

HABITAT: in well-drained meadows, beside paths, especially at an altitude of over 1,670 ft (500 m). Fall. Common to uncommon but widespread.

DESCRIPTION: H: 1$^{1}/_{2}$-3$^{1}/_{4}$ in (4-8 cm), Ø: 1$^{1}/_{4}$-3$^{1}/_{4}$ in (3-8 cm).
Cap convex at first but soon flattening and ending with an upturned margin and a large central umbo. Flesh thick in the center, thin at the edge. Slightly greasy to the touch, apricot or salmon pink. Thick, wide,

EDIBILITY
Good to eat.

CUPHOPHYLLUS VIRGINEUS, HYGROPHORUS NIVEUS
Snow-white Wax-cap

DESCRIPTION: H: 1$^{1}/_{2}$-3$^{1}/_{4}$ in (4-8 cm), Ø: $^{1}/_{2}$-1$^{1}/_{2}$ in (1-4 cm).
Cap conical and umbonate at first, then flattening, often with a central depression; fleshy under the center, pure white,

occasional ocher or reddish spots. White gills

EDIBILITY
Good to eat.

very wide apart and decurrent. Stipe long and sinuous, white shaded with pink or red at the base. Flesh white.

HABITAT: meadows and pastures, mossy lawns, grassy moors, and damp, grassy woods where it is frequently con-fined to the edges. From fall through early winter. Common and widespread.

POTENTIAL CONFUSION
▶ *CLITOCYBE DEALBATA, C. RIVULOSA, C. CANDICANS* White Clitocybes POISONOUS

HYGROCYBE PSITTACINA

Parrot Wax-cap

DESCRIPTION: H:1½-2¾ in (4-7 cm), Ø:¾-1½ in (2-4 cm).
Hemispherical or campanulate cap becom-ing convex or flattened, umbonate, with striated margin. Very viscid, blue-green dis-coloring with age to yellow orange; the cap may be multicolored. Gills slightly emarginate, yellowish-green or orange. Stipe solid at first, then hollow, and with the same vis-cosity and coloration as the cap, green at first, then yellowing from the base. Yellow-green flesh thin, odorless and flavorless.

HABITAT: meadows, pastures, roadsides, in lowlands and highlands. Summer through late fall. Uncommon.

SPECIAL FEATURES
The *Hygrocybe* are brightly colored Wax Caps which grow in grassland. Many of them appear to be becoming less numerous.

HYGROCYBE CHLOROPHANA

Lemon Wax-cap

DESCRIPTION: H:1¼-3 in (3-7 cm), Ø:1¼-3 in (3-7 cm).
Convex cap, flattening, retaining a central umbo and becoming slightly depressed. Margin may be striated, viscid, golden then sulfur yellow. Pale yellow gills, widely spaced and bowed. Stipe thin, becoming hollow, fragile, and slightly viscid. Thin, pale yellow flesh and odorless, mild flavor.

HABITAT: groups in grassland and the edge of woodland and beside hedges in summer through fall. Uncommon but widespread.

SPECIAL FEATURES

Hygrophorus obrusseus is another golden-yellow hygrophorus, but the cap remains conical and the stipe is not viscid.

HYGROCYBE COCCINEA

Scarlet Wax-cap

DESCRIPTION:
H: 1¾-3¼ in (4-8 cm),
Ø: ¾-2 in (2-5 cm).
Convex cap, blood-red at first, then turning pink as it ages. Widely-spaced gills, reddish orange then turning yellower, always yellow at the edges. Stem hollow, slightly compressed, often with a longitudinal furrow, orange-red but yellow at the base. Flesh thin, golden-yellow to red; faint odor and mild flavor which is hard to define.

HABITAT: grows in troops on grassland and at the edge of forests. Summer and fall. Uncommon, more frequently found at higher altitudes. Widespread.

THE TRICHOLOMATALES

HYGROCYBE MINIATA
Vermillion Wax-cap

DESCRIPTION: H: $^3/_4$-2 in (2-5 cm), Ø: $^1/_2$-$1^1/_4$ in (1-3 cm).
Cap hemispherical at first, then convex or flattened, more or less depressed in the center, with striated margin covered in tiny tightly-packed scales, vermillion then turning yellow. Gills the same color. Hollow, brittle stipe with smooth, matte, dry surface, red with an orange-yellow to pale yellow base. Flesh orange and odorless, mild flavor.

HABITAT: lawns and heaths, on acid soil, especially in the mountains. Fairly common and widespread.

HYGROPHORUS COSSUS
Stinking Wax-cap

DESCRIPTION: H:2-4 in (5-10 cm), Ø:$1^1/_4$-$3^1/_4$ in (3-8 cm).
The cap is hemispherical and conical, then flattened, with a smooth, viscid surface, white to cream, turning yellow or brown-ish-ocher in the center with age. Gills broad and cream-colored. Stipe narrowing at the base, viscid, with flakes adhering at the top, creamy white, yellowing with age. Thick white flesh with unpleasant smell and mild flavor.

SPECIAL FEATURES

This Wax-cap resembles the Ivory Wax-cap but is more slender; the unpleasant odor of cooked Jerusalem artichokes makes it distinctive. The botanical epithet *"cossus"* comes from the name of a moth whose caterpillar has the same unpleasant odor as the mushroom.

HABITAT: deciduous forests, especially oak and mixed woods. Commoner in warmer climates, on limestone soils. Fall.

HYGROPHORUS EBURNEUS

Ivory Wax-cap

DESCRIPTION: H:2³/₈-4³/₄ in (6-12 cm), Ø:4¹/₂-4 (4-10 cm). Hemispherical or conical cap, becoming flattened and more or less undulating, with margin which remains inrolled for a long time. Very viscid, pure white, then cream-tinted. Thick, white, widely spaced gills, slightly decurrent. Long, white, viscid stipe, thinner at the base, often curving, granulose or floccose at the top. Flesh thin and white, aromatic but faint odor, mild, pleasant flavor.

HABITAT: often grows in colonies in deciduous forests, especially beech woods, on non-acidic soil. Early through late fall. Fairly common.

HYGROPHORUS HYPOTHEJUS

Yellow-gilled Wax-cap

DESCRIPTION: H:2¹/₂-4 in (6-10 cm), Ø:1¹/₄-2³/₄ in (3-7 cm). Cap convex or campanulate at first, then flattening and become slightly depressed in the center, with or without an umbo, margin remaining inrolled for a long time. Cap fibrillose, very viscid, olive-brown paling to yellow-ocher as it dries. Gills widely spaced, decurrent, white turning progressively bright yellow-orange. Stipe long and thin, very viscid, except at the top, white then yellowish-orange. Flesh thick, white, yellowish-orange under the cuticle, odorless with mild flavor.

HABITAT: coniferous forests, mainly pinewoods, on acidic soils. It appears late, after the first frosts, in late fall and early winter. Fairly common and widespread.

HYGROPHORUS MARZUOLUS

March Wax-cap

DESCRIPTION: H1^1/$_2$-3^1/$_4$ in (4-8 cm), Ø:2-4^1/$_2$ in (5-12 cm).
Cap thick, hemispherical at first then convex or flattened, or slightly depressed, umbonate, with a margin that remains inrolled for a long time. White when young, turning grayish and eventually blackish. Gills thick, straight, slightly decurrent, white then graying, becoming wider apart with age. Stipe thick and short, full, white then turning gray like the rest of the fungus. Flesh thick and white, odorless with a mild flavor.

HABITAT: in small groups in coniferous forests, mainly fir, pine, and spruce. It is often hidden by moss or pine-needle litter. On limestone soil at mid-mountain altitude, but also in the lowlands in more northerly regions. Late winter, lingering on into spring in some regions. Fairly common to rare, depending on the region.

SPECIAL FEATURES

Some people find it is not particularly tasty and claim that its only virtue is that it appears in early winter and spring, when edible mushrooms are at their rarest.

EDIBILITY

Edible, though there is some dispute as to whether it is worth eating.

HYGROPHORUS OLIVACEOALBUS

Olive Wax-cap

DESCRIPTION: H: 4-6 in (10-15 cm), Ø: 2-2³/₄ in (5-8 cm).
Hemispherical or campanulate cap, becoming convex or flattened with an umbo, very viscid, olive-brown, darkening in the center. Gills decurrent and bow-shaped, waxy, white to pale gray. Stipe tall and slender (4-6 in (10-15 cm)), very viscid, covered in olive-brown stripes, except at the top which is white and dry, the two zones being separated by a fairly distinct ring. Whitish flesh, thick only in the center; odor and flavor not characteristic.

EDIBILITY

Not particularly good, and the viscid cuticle should be peeled off.

HABITAT: under spruce, growing among bilberries, blueberries, and moss, on acid soils. Common in the late summer and fall.

THE TRICHOLOMATALES

HYGROPHORUS PUDORINUS
Modest Wax-cap

DESCRIPTION: H: 3¹/₄-4¹/₂ in (8-12 cm), Ø: 3¹/₄-5 in (8-13 cm).
Cap hemispherical then convex with inrolled margin, fleshy, very viscid in damp weather, matte and silky in dry weather, pale ochraceous-orange to fawn, darker in the center and creamy pink at the margin. Gills broad and widely spaced, bow-shaped and only slightly decurrent, white at first then of a color similar to that of the cap. Stipe slightly bulbous, thick (up to 1¹/₄ in (3 cm)), slightly viscid at first, the same color as the gills and browning slightly at the base, dotted with pinkish-white granulations at the top. Flesh white, pinkish under the cuticle of the cap, with a resinous odor. Flavor mild to slightly acrid or strongly resinous.

EDIBILITY

Some specimens have such a strongly resinous flavor that they are inedible. Others are merely of poor edibility.

HABITAT: under conifers, especially spruce and fir, on non-acidic soil, and even limestone. Commoner on high ground.

HYGROPHORUS RUSSULA
Russula Wax-cap

then dry, pinkish, rapidly becoming covered in dark pink spots. Gills tightly packed, wide, non-decurrent, white or pale pink, becoming spotted with darker pink. Stipe thick, up to 1¾ in (4 cm) in diameter, the same color as the cap, covered in longitudinal purple fibers, granulose at the top. Flesh pale or spotted with dark red spots, pleasant fruity odor, mild or slightly bitter flavor.

DESCRIPTION: H:3¼-6 in (8-15 cm), Ø:3¼-6 in (8-15 cm).
Cap hemispherical then convex, fleshy, can attain 8 in (20 cm) in diameter, viscid at first,

HABITAT: often in groups under deciduous trees such as oak and beech, on limestone soil. Summer and fall. Fairly common in more southerly regions.

PLEUROTUS CORNUCOPIAE
Branched Oyster Mushroom

DESCRIPTION: H:¾-4 in (2-10 cm), Ø:1½-4½ in (4-12 cm).
Funnel-shaped cap, of uniform color, creamy white or beige, darkening with age. Creamy gills very decurrent, bonded together at the base of the stipe to form a network. Stipe central or excentric. Odor pleasant, flavor mild.

EDIBILITY
Very good to eat.

HABITAT: singly or more often in tufts on stumps or the dead branches of various deciduous trees (elm, willow, poplar, oak, beech, etc.). May through August. Fairly common in the south, rarer in the north.

PLEUROTUS ERYNGII

Eryngo Oyster Mushroom

DESCRIPTION: H:1¹/₄-3¹/₄ in (3-8 cm), Ø:2-4¹/₂ in (5-12 cm).
Cap convex then flattening, margin almost always inrolled, smooth, beige to brown. Gills quite widely spaced, decurrent, creamy white or reddening. Stipe excentric or central, usually curved, white and velvety. Flesh white, quite firm, pleasant flavor and odor.

HABITAT: in dry, meadows on poor soil and and fallow land. Develops on the dead roots of eryngo and sea-holly, near coasts. Spring through fall. Fairly common along the coast and in southern regions.

EDIBILITY
Very good to eat.

PLEUROTUS OSTREATUS

Oyster Mushroom

DESCRIPTION: H:1¼-4 in (3-10 cm), Ø:2-6 in (5-15 cm). Cap spatulate at first, extending to look more like a mollusk shell, with a margin which remains inrolled for a long time and a smooth surface with a color that varies but is uniform, often slate gray or gray-brown, becoming paler with age. The very decurrent gills are ivory in color. Lateral stipe, more or less curved, generally very short, velvety at the base. Flesh white with a pleasant odor and flavor.

HABITAT: forms compact tufts of tiered specimens on logs or the dead trunks of various deciduous trees, such as poplar, willow, walnut, oak, and beech. From fall through early winter and during the winter in southerly regions. Fairly common and widespread.

EDIBILITY

Good to eat. Should be picked young as it often becomes worm-eaten and coriaceous with age.

SPECIAL FEATURES

The oyster mushroom is now cultivated all over the world. It is grown intensively in a manner similar to that of the Cultivated Mushroom.

LENTINUS COCHLEATUS

Spiral Lentinus

DESCRIPTION: H:1¹/₂-4 in (4-10 cm), Ø:1¹/₄-3¹/₄ in (3-8 cm). The cap is continuous with the stipe, giving the mushroom the shape of a cornet that is notched on one side. The margin is inrolled and is fawn or reddish brown in color. The gills are strongly decurrent, saw-

edged and cream to brownish. The stipe is central or excentric and the same color as the cap at the top, darker at the base. The flesh is thick and coriaceous, whitish to beige, with a mild aniseed odor and flavor.

HABITAT: in dense, tiered tufts on stumps and at the base of trunks of deciduous trees. Late summer and fall.

LENTINUS TIGRINUS

Striped Lentinus

DESCRIPTION: H: 1¹/₂-3¹/₄ in (4-8 cm), Ø: 1¹/₂-4 in (4-10 cm). Cap globose at first, becoming convex, and finally depressed in the center, with a thin, sinuous, inrolled margin that is often split; the background color is cream, covered with brown or black scales arranged in a fairly regular pattern, more densely in the center. Gills decurrent and tightly packed, with an irregularly emarginate edge, creamy white then tinted orange. Stipe more or less excentric, thinning toward the base, whitish and brown toward the bottom, scaly like the cap. Flesh whitish, elastic. Odor fruity, flavor mild at first, becoming acrid.

HABITAT: often grows in tufts on willow and poplar, frequently beside water. From spring through fall. Uncommon but widespread.

EDIBILITY

Fairly good to eat when young, too coriaceous when older.

PANELLUS SEROTINUS
Winter Panellus

DESCRIPTION: Ø:1¼-4 in (3-10 cm). Shell-shaped or spatulate fungus, with a yellow-green or brownish cap, velvety but very viscid in wet weather with a margin which is inrolled at first. Gills tightly packed and forked, pale yellow then pale ocher. Stipe lateral, very short, ochraceous orange and covered in small brown scales. Whitish flesh thick, soft, and elastic; faint odor and mild flavor.

HABITAT: in tiered clumps, on branches and dead or living tree-trunks, especially wil-

low and alder, in damp places, especially beside waterways. Late fall and winter. Fairly common.

DESCRIPTION: Ø: ½-1½ in (1-4 cm). Semi-circular cap, depressed where attached to the stipe, with inrolled, striated or fur-

PANELLUS STIPTICUS
Styptic Mushroom

rowed margin, ocher or pale brown. Felted surface, cracking with age. Russet gills crowded and often forked. Stipe excentric or lateral, very short (¾ in (2 cm) at the most) and thinning toward the base, paler than the cap. Flesh soft and elastic, whitish or pale yellow, aromatic odor but bitter, acrid flavor.

HABITAT: in dense, tiered clumps on dead wood, fallen branches, and the stumps of deciduous trees, mainly oak. All year round, but mainly in the fall. Common.

THE TRICHOLOMATALES

OMPHALINA ERICETORUM, GERRONEMA ERICETORUM
Moss Omphalia

DESCRIPTION: H: $^3/_4$-2 in (2-5 cm), Ø: $^1/_3$-$^3/_4$ in (0.7-2 cm).
Convex cap, soon becoming funnel-shaped in the center, undulating or sinuate margin; surface striated to the center or with darker radial bands over the gills. White-beige, to pale ocher or yellow-brown in color. Gills decurrent, widely spaced and thick, but thinning toward the edge of the cap, cream to pale yellow. Stipe thin and short ($^1/_2$ to 1$^1/_4$ in (1 to 3 cm)), pale brown, darker at the top. Flesh thin and pale, odorless and flavorless.

SPECIAL FEATURES

This is one of the commonest fungi in the northern hemisphere. It lives in moss, in symbiosis with an alga.

HABITAT: in colder regions, especially in the mountains, on damp, acidic soil, heathland and beside bogs. Summer through fall. Common and widespread.

PSEUDOCLITOCYBE CYATHIFORMIS
Cup-shaped Clitocybe

DESCRIPTION: H: 2¾-4¾ in (7-12 cm),
Ø: 1¾-2¾ in (3-7 cm).
Cap cup-shaped, with small umbo and inrolled margin, dark brown, almost black when wet, becoming much paler as it dries. Gills decurrent and forked, with crenelated edges, white turning pale grayish-beige. . Very long stipe thickening toward the base, brown and striated with paler fibrils. Base felted with white fibers. Flesh thin and spongy; pleasant odor and mild flavor.

HABITAT: forests, grassy paths, on the ground or on rotten tree stumps. Late fall. Common.

shorter gills inserted between long ones

very long, stipe striated with whitish fibrils.

SPECIAL FEATURES

The Pseudoclitocybes differ from the Clitocybes due to their forked gills.

CLITOCYBE CANDICANS

White Clitocybe

DESCRIPTION: H:1¼-1½ in (3-4 cm), Ø:¾-1¼ in (2-3 cm).
Cap convex then flattening and slightly depressed, pure white, later dirty white or spotted with ocher or brown. Margin inrolled for a long time. White gills crowded and slightly decurrent. White stipe elastic, often bent, covered in white flakes on the upper third. Flesh thin and white; pleasant odor and mild flavor.

HABITAT: lawns, grassy clearings, under deciduous trees or in copses. Summer through fall. Fairly common.

TOXICITY
Very poisonous.

CLITOCYBE CERRUSSATA
Hoary Clitocybe

DESCRIPTION: H: 2-4 in (5-10 cm),
Ø: 1¼-3¼ in (3-8 cm).
Cap convex then flattening, eventually
slightly depressed, margin inrolled for a
long time. Silky surface with a white
coating like hoar-frost, dispersing with
age to reveal a pinkish or ocher ground.
Crowded, slightly decurrent, white or cream

TOXICITY
Poisonous.

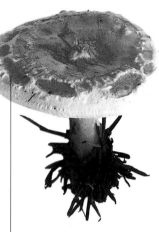

hoary white coating on pale ocher background

gills. Stipe white, often curved, solid then
hollow, wider at the base which is covered
with a white down which holds the leaf litter around the base. Flesh blanche; slightly
floury odor, mild flavor.

HABITAT: coniferous forests from summer
through early fall. Fairly common.

SPECIAL FEATURES
Clitocybe Phyllophila is similar in every respect, but grows under deciduous trees, and has been classified as a separate species. It is equally dangerous.

CLITOCYBE DEALBATA
Ivory Mushroom

DESCRIPTION: H:1¼-2½ in
(3-6 cm), Ø:¾-2 in (2-5 cm).
Cap convex, soon flattening,
and even becoming slightly
depressed, margin inrolled.
White, matte and silky, covered in a coating like hoar-
frost, marked in places with
beige or pale brown, shaded
with pink. Gills crowded,
slightly decurrent, whitish
then reddening. Stipe short,
often slightly bent at the
base and elastic, whitish or
beige. Flesh thin and white,
slightly floury odor, mild
flavor.

HABITAT: in troops or rings
in pastures, on lawns, beside
hedgerows, and on playing-
fields. Summer through fall.
Common.

SPECIAL FEATURES

The white species of Clitocybe are very
hard to tell apart. *Clitocybe rivulosa* is
more distinctive, in that it is less white,
taller, and has no odor of flour.

TOXICITY

Very poisonous.

CLITOCYBE VIBECINA
Striated Agaric

DESCRIPTION: H:2-3$\frac{1}{4}$ in (5-8 cm), Ø:1$\frac{1}{4}$-2$\frac{1}{2}$ in (3-6 cm).
Cap convex with inrolled margin, slightly striated when mature; smooth, gray-brown when wet, discoloring to pale gray as it dries, starting in the center. Gills slightly decurrent, pale gray or brown. Stipe solid then hollow, gray, with longitudinal white fibrils, white cottony fibers at the base. Flesh thin, gray to brown, faint floury or rancid odor, mild flavor.

HABITAT: coniferous and mixed forests. From mid-fall through early winter. Fairly common.

CLITOCYBE GIBBA
Funnel-shaped Clitocybe

DESCRIPTION: H:2-4 in (5-10 cm), Ø:1$\frac{1}{2}$-4 in (4-10 cm).
Umbonate cap with inrolled margin, then funnel-shaped in the center with faintly striated margin, becoming more or less sinuous. May retain slight umbo. Cream-

thin, full then hollow, whitish or pale russet; the base is surrounded by leaf litter felted together with a fluffy white mycelium. Thin, white flesh, faint but pleasant odor, mild flavor.

HABITAT: in troops in deciduous and coniferous forests, in lowland or at altitude. Summer through fall. Very common.

EDIBILITY
Quite good to eat, as long as the fibrous stem is discarded.

colored, beige or pale russet. White, crowded gills, very decurrent. Stipe fairly

CLITOCYBE DECEMBRIS

Two-colored Agaric

DESCRIPTION: H:1¹/₂-3¹/₄ in (4-8 cm), Ø:1¹/₄-2¹/₂ in (3-6 cm).
Cap convex, with an umbilicus in the center, sometimes becoming funnel-shaped. Gray-brown when wet, beige to pale brown during dry spells, but very often with a darker patch in the center. Gills more or less decurrent, yellow-gray or pale brown. Stipe twisted and rigid, paler, with white fibrils, turning darker gray at the base. Flesh thin and whitish; faint odor, mild flavor.

HABITAT: deciduous or coniferous woods, from fall through winter. Very common.

CLITOCYBE CLAVIPES
Club-footed Agaric

DESCRIPTION: H:2¹/₂-4 in (6-10 cm), Ø: 1¹/₂-2³/₄ in (4-7 cm).
Cap convex then flattened, with a slight umbo, becoming funnel-shaped in older specimens, gray-brown with a darker center and paler at the margin. Gills decurrent, widely spaced, cream or pale yellow. Stipe swollen at the base, twice as thick as at the top, ocher to brown, striated. Flesh spongy, especially at the center of the cap and base of the stipe. Strong odor and mild flavor.

HABITAT: coniferous forests, on acid soil, in the plains or mountains. Late summer and fall. Very common.

CLITOCYBE ODORA
Aniseed Mushroom

DESCRIPTION: H:1¹/₂-4 in (4-10 cm), Ø:1¹/₄-3¹/₄ in (4-8 cm).
Cap convex at first with an inrolled margin, sometimes umbonate, then flattening, with an undulating. slightly retracted margin. Matte blue-green in young specimens, turning grayish-green or gray-brown in others. Gills very slightly decurrent, dirty white, then gray green. Stipe whitish, fibrillose, then taking on the color of the cap, and with a white down around the base. Flesh white and soft, strong aniseed odor and flavor.

EDIBILITY

Edible but with strong aniseed flavor.

HABITAT: in deciduous forests (mostly beech and birch) or under conifers (mainly spruce) from plains to mountains. Summer through fall. Fairly common.

CLITOCYBE NEBULARIS

Clouded Agaric

DESCRIPTION: H:2³/₄-6 in (7-15 cm), Ø:3¹/₄-8 in (8-20 cm).
Cap convex then flattened may become depressed, with or without a small umbo and a margin which remains inrolled for a long time. Surface gray or gray-brown, dark at first, then paler, covered in a sort of cottony veil. Gills crowded, slightly decurrent, white to pale yellow. Stipe thick, soon becoming hollow with age, grayish-white, covered in gray fibrils, base swollen, but hidden in leaf litter. White mycelium accumulates leaf litter around the stipe. Flesh white and soft, strong but in definable odor, flavor mild or slightly bitter.

HABITAT: often grows in rings in deciduous or coniferous forests, sometimes in parks. In fall and often late into the winter. Very common and widespread.

TOXICITY

Although considered edible, the species should be rejected as it can cause serious digestive problems.

CLITOCYBE GEOTROPA

Monk's Head Agaric

DESCRIPTION: H:4-10 in (10-25 cm), Ø:2¹/₂-8 in (6-20 cm).
Cap more or less flat and umbonate, then becoming funnel-shaped while retaining the central umbo, pinkish-beige or flesh-colored. Gills very decurrent, cream or beige. Stipe thick and smooth, thickening from top to bottom, the same color as the cap. Flesh white, thick in the center, thin at the edge of the cap; strong odor of bitter almonds, mild flavor.

HABITAT: in circles or rows in well-lit deciduous woods, clearings, wooded pastures, in hilly or mountainous country, on non-acidic or limestone soil. Fall. Fairly common.

EDIBILITY

Good to eat when young; the stem is too fibrous and should be discarded.

LEPISTA INVERSA

Inside Out Agaric

DESCRIPTION: H:2-4 in (5-10 cm), Ø:1¹/₂-4 in (4-10 cm).
Cap rapidly becoming funnel-shaped, but with a thin, tightly inrolled margin, orange or reddish, often sprinkled with reddish-brown patches as it ages. Gills very crowded and decurrent, cream then orange. Short stipe 2 in (5 cm) maximum), the same color as the cap, with a white downy base surrounded by leaf litter.

HABITAT: in dense clumps in coniferous wood in lowland and highland. Summer through late fall. Very frequent and widespread.

EDIBILITY

Fairly good to eat.

LEPISTA PANAEOLUS, L. LUSCINA

Cloudy Tricholoma

DESCRIPTION: H:1¹/₂-2³/₄ in (4-7 cm), Ø: 1¹/₄-4 in (3-10 cm).
Cap thick, convex, with a slight central depression, soon flattening and long retaining the inrolled margin; gray-beige, with small round, darker oily or waxy scattered at random or in rings around the edge. Gills white then grayish-pink. Stipe short, 2 in (5 cm) maximum, dirty white. Flesh thick, whitish, smelling strongly of flour, flavor mild but not particularly pleasant.

EDIBILITY

Good to eat, with a spicy flavor when cooked, but often worm-eaten.

HABITAT: In small groups in mountain pastures. Fall. Fairly common.

THE TRICHOLOMATALES

LEPISTA NUDA
Wood Blewit

DESCRIPTION: H:2½-4½ in (6-12 cm), Ø:2-6 in (5-15 cm).
Cap thick and smooth, becoming depressed in the center, margin inrolled for a long time, blue-violet at first, but may lose all trace of violet color with age. Gills crowded, amethyst color, darker than the cap. Stipe thick (1½ to 4 in x ⅛ to 1¼ in (4 to 10 cm x 1.5 to 3 cm)), wider at the base, the same color as the gills, covered in silvery fibrils. Flesh thick, friable, slightly fibrous in the stipe, pale lilac; strong, fruity odor, smelling slightly of aniseed and mild flavor.

HABITAT: in groups or circles in deciduous woods (beech, chestnut, oak) or among conifers. From late fall to early winter, but appearing earlier at altitude. Very common, but requiring low temperatures. The species grows almost throughout the year, especially in spring and from late summer.

lilac-colored flesh

EDIBILITY

Very good to eat, but requires fairly prolonged cooking as the flesh is tough. The Wood Blewit can be cultivated.

LEPISTA SORDIDA
Lesser Blue-Foot

DESCRIPTION: H:1½-2½ in (4-6 cm), Ø: 1¼-2¾ in (3-7 cm).
Cap slightly depressed in the center, with a small umbo, thin, slightly inrolled margin, dark bluish violet, darkening with age. Pale lilac gills. Stipe no more than ½ in (1 cm) in diameter, the same color as the cap.

violet gills and stipe

HABITAT: meadows, smoky places, conifer plantations, gardens, avenues. Late summer and fall. Uncommon.

EDIBILITY
Fairly good to eat.

LEPISTA SAEVA, L. PERSONATA
Blewit

DESCRIPTION: H:2-4½ in (5-12 cm), Ø:3¼-6 in (8-15 cm).

Hemispherical cap, becoming convex, then flattened, coffee or beige color, smooth, matte surface. Stipe short and thick, from ¾ to 1¼ in (2 to 3 cm) in diameter, swollen at the base, fibrillose, blue-violet, contrasting with the darker color of the gills and cap. Flesh thick, white, or pinkish-beige; faint but pleasant odor, mild flavor.

HABITAT: in circles in meadows and parks, on limestone soil. From late fall to early winter. Fairly common in places.

EDIBILITY
Good to eat.

ARMILLARIA MELLEA

Honey Fungus

DESCRIPTION: H:$2^{3}/_{4}$-8 in (7-20 cm), Ø:$1^{1}/_{4}$-4 in (3-10 cm).
The cap is hemispherical and scaly at first, becoming flattened and wavy with scales that are widely separated or absent. The color is very variable, honey-color or yellow-brown. The gills are white, slightly decurrent, with reddish spots. The stipe is very long and smooth, except at the whitish, striated top. It has a fragile, cottony white ring. Strong, unpleasant odor.

HABITAT: forms large tufts on stumps or fallen branches of deciduous trees, especially beech. Sometimes parasitizes living trees. Fall. Very common.

SPECIAL FEATURES

The Honey Fungus is a dangerous parasite which attacks living or weakened trees, causing heart-rot. It propagates by means of ramified black filaments which run beneath the bark of the trunks or branches. These filaments, which are merely bunches of mycelium, look like thin roots and for this reason they are called rhizomorphs or pseudorrhiza.

EDIBILITY/TOXICITY

The Honey Fungus is not necessarily edible, because older or undercooked specimens have produced poisonings. Specimens for the table should be very young and the fibrous stem must be discarded. Despite these precautions, some people cannot digest the Honey Fungus which is widely eaten in Eastern Europe, Italy, and Spain.

ARMILLARIA OSTOYAE

Darkening Armillaria

DESCRIPTION: H:2³/₄-6 in (7-15 cm), Ø: 1¹/₂-4 in (4-10 cm).

Cap conical or convex, then flattened and undulating. The surface is covered with dark brown scales, crowded in the center, on a brown or reddish-brown background. Margin striated, paler than the rest of the cap, and with more widely spaced scales. Gills white or cream, becoming spotted with reddish-brown patches. Stipe brittle, solid, becoming hollow, ocher but darker toward the base, striated above the white ring edged with darker flakes.

HABITAT: in tufts on tree-stumps or the roots of spruce or fir. Summer and fall. Common.

CATATHELASMA VENTRICOSA

Bulbous-stemmed Armillaria

lower one membranous, the upper one downy. Flesh compact, thick and white.

HABITAT: isolated or in groups under conifers, especially firs, in North America. Late summer and fall. Common.

DESCRIPTION: H:2³/₄-6 in (7-15 cm), Ø:3¹/₄-6 in (8-15 cm).

Convex cap dry and smooth, whitish or pale gray. Gills slightly decurrent, whitish or pale brown. Thick stipe (1 to 2 in (2.5 to 5 cm)), deeply buried in the soil, white to yellowish-brown with a characteristic double ring, the

EDIBILITY

Quite good to eat. A similar species which is also edible is found in Europe, the Imperial Armillaria *(Catathelasma imperialis.* It is larger with a darker cap.

LACCARIA AMETHYSTEA
Amethyst Deceiver

DESCRIPTION: H:2-4¹/₂ in (5-12 cm), Ø:³/₄-2¹/₂ in (2-6 cm).
Cap convex then flattened, thin with an inrolled margin, then undulating and sometimes slightly crenelated, often umbilicate in the center. Amethyst, turning to pale lilac, almost white or ochraceous violet when dry; the surface is matte, granulose, or covered with fine scales toward the center. The wide, deep violet gills are thick and widely spaced, interspersed with shorter gills. They are sprinkled with white spores when mature. The stipe is long, thin, sinuous and fibrous, the same color as the cap, often consisting of whitish fibrils and with lilac felting at the base. The thin, violet flesh is elastic in the stipe, and has a mild odor and flavor which are not characteristic.

HABITAT: coniferous or deciduous forests, on acid or limestone soil, mainly in hilly or mountainous regions. From late summer through fall. Very common.

gills bright amethyst in color

SPECIAL FEATURES

The deep amethyst violet color in young specimens make it easy to recognize the Amethyst Deceiver growing on moss or leaf litter. The cap is good to eat but the fibrous stem should be discarded. At one time the Amethyst Deceiver was merely considered to be a variety of the Deceiver (*Laccaria laccata*), a closely related species.

EDIBILITY

Good to eat.

LACCARIA LACCATA

Deceiver

depressed cap, margin downward facing

DESCRIPTION: H:2-4 in (5-10 cm), Ø:³/₄-1¹/₂ in (2-4 cm).
Cap domed then convex and depressed in the center. The edge remains curved downward for a long time. Color is russet, pinkish-orange, or brownish-orange, paling when dry or with aging. Surface matte, smooth, or slightly grainy. Gills wide, pinkish-brown. Stipe thin and elastic, reddish-brown with white fibrils. Flesh whitish to brownish, depending on the degree of humidity. Odor faint and flavor mild.

HABITAT: deciduous or coniferous forests and copses. Late summer through fall. Common and widespread.

SPECIAL FEATURES

There are various varieties or similar species to the Deceiver.

EDIBILITY

Quite good to eat.

TRICHOLOMOPSIS DECORA
Elegant Tricholoma

DESCRIPTION: H:2-3¼ in (5-8 cm), Ø:2-6 in (5-15 cm).
Bright yellow or yellow-ocher cap with fine gray-brown scales or fibrils, denser in the center, conical at first, then convex or flattened. The margin remains inrolled for a long time. Gills bright yellow with white edges. Stipe long and thin, often excentric or curved,fibrillose, the same color as the cap or paler. Flesh bright yellow, no particular odor or flavor.

HABITAT: singly or in tufts, on coniferous stumps, twigs, or tree trunks mainly in the mountains. Late summer through late fall. Uncommon.

SPECIAL FEATURES
T. ornata and *T. flammula* are smaller fungi with reddish-brown scales.

TRICHOLOMOPSIS RUTILANS
Plums and Custard

DESCRIPTION: H:2½-4½ in (6-12 cm), Ø:2-4½ in (5-12 cm).
Cap conical or domed, then flattened, velvety and covered with fine, brick-red or purplish scales on a yellow background, hence the name. Gills crowded and egg yellow; stipe thickening at the base, sometimes curved, yellow and speckled with red scales less dense than those on the cap. Pale yellow flesh, slightly bitter, or mild.

EDIBILITY
Despite its name this fungus is not considered edible in western Europe, though it is eaten in certain parts of eastern Europe.

HABITAT: in tufts on the rotten stumps of conifers (pine trees) or on the trunks. From late summer through fall. Fairly common and widespread.

TRICHOLOMA COLUMBETTA
Dove-like Tricholoma

DESCRIPTION:
H:3¹/₄-5 in (8-13 cm), Ø:2-4 in (5-10 cm).
Cap convex or conical at first, soon
flattening, then becoming
more or less undulating ,
sometimes with a cen-
tral swelling. Often
inclined, and pure
white in color,
sometimes spotted with tiny, reddish-pink or blue-green marks. The
center may be pale ocher. The silky
and satiny surface is covered in fine
radial fibrils and is slightly viscid when
wet, often becoming covered in traces of
soil. Gills crowded and white, toothed at the
edges. Stipe sturdy, slightly spindle-shaped,
full and firm, fibrillose. Flesh firm and white,
with an odor and taste of flour.

silky surface of the cap

completely white mushroom

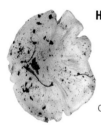

HABITAT: deciduous
woods, mainly under
oaks, sometimes under
conifers, on non-acidic
or sandy soil. Summer
through fall. Fairly
common in places.

EDIBILITY
Good to eat.

POTENTIAL CONFUSION

▶ *AMANITA VIROSA*
Destroying Angel   DEADLY

▶ *AMANITA VERNA*
Spring Amanita   DEADLY

▶ *AMANITA PHALLOIDES*
White Death Cap   DEADLY

▶ *ENTOLOMA LIVIDUM*
Livid Entoloma   POISONOUS

TRICHOLOMA ALBUM

White Tricholoma

DESCRIPTION: H:2¹/₂-4 in (6-10 cm), Ø:1¹/₂-2¹/₂ in (4-6 cm).
Cap domed or conical, then flattened, matte chalky white. Gills wide and can be seen in vertical section to be of unequal width, white then pale ocher. Stipe white, elongated and flexing, solid, slightly swollen at the base, or tapering. Flesh thin and white, with a faintly acrid odor and flavor.

HABITAT: under deciduous trees, especially birch, in acid soil. Late summer through fall. Common.

SPECIAL FEATURES

The Off-white Tricholoma *(Tricholoma pseudoalbum)* can measure up to 6 in (15 cm) in diameter. The margin is fluted. It is completely white, browning slightly to the touch and emits a strong and disagreeable odor. The flavor is very acrid. It grows among oaks and hornbeam. *Tricholoma lascivum* has a beige or pale ocher cap and smells pleasantly of flour.

TRICHOLOMA FULVUM
Fawn Tricholoma

DESCRIPTION: H:3¹/₄-5 in (8-13 cm), Ø:2-4 in (5-10 cm).

Cap conical or convex then flattened, umbonate or slightly depressed, with an inrolled, striated or fluted margin. Smooth, viscid in the young state or when wet, reddish-brown with a paler margin and yellow tints. Gills bright yellow becoming tinged with dirty rust with age. Stipe of the same color as the cap, or yellower. Flesh white in the cap but characteristically yellow in the stipe, smelling of flour and with a slightly bitter taste.

HABITAT: in small groups of deciduous or mixed woods, especially under birch, on very damp, acidic soil. On lowland and highland. Late summer through fall. Very common and widespread.

SPECIAL FEATURES

Tricholoma pseudonictitans, which tends to appear under conifers, does not have a fluted margin and the gills are whitish splashed with rust.

TOXICITY

Suspected of being poisonous.

TRICHOLOMA USTALE

Bitter Tricholoma

DESCRIPTION: H:2-4 in (5-10 cm), Ø:1¹/₂-3¹/₄ in (4-8 cm).

SPECIAL FEATURES

The Tawny Tricholoma *(Tricholoma ustaloides)* resembles the Burnt Tricholoma, but the cap is brighter russet, and the two-colored stipe has two clear areas of color, white at the top and russet below. It exudes a strongly floury odor.

Cap hemispherical or conical then convex or flattened, with an inrolled, sinuous margin, reddish-brown then paler at the margin. Gills white then spotted with red. Stipe white and larger at the base which turns brown with age. Pale colored flesh, darker at the base of the stipe; faintly floury odor and slightly bitter taste.

HABITAT: deciduous woods (beech) on damp, non-acidic soil. From late summer through fall. Fairly common.

TRICHOLOMA VACCINUM
Brindle Tricholoma

DESCRIPTION: H:2½-4 in (6-10 cm), Ø: 1½-3¼ in (4-8 cm).

Cap domed to conical, then flattening to slightly umbonate, covered with reddish-brown, woolly or fibrillose, dense, crowded scales, thinning out at the edge;against a pale ocher background; Margin woolly and slightly inrolled. Gills wide, toothed, cream then splashed with pink. Stipe hollow, taller than the diameter of the cap, swollen at the base which can attain ¾ in (2 cm) in diameter, and the same color as the cap. Flesh thin and whitish, except at the base of the stipe where it is reddish-brown and under the cuticle where it is pinkish. Rather unpleasant floury smell, bitter flavor.

HABITAT: under conifers, rarely under deciduous trees, mainly in the mountains. Fall. Common.

TRICHOLOMA PORTENTOSUM

Pretentious Tricholoma

DESCRIPTION: H: 2½-4½ in (6-12 cm), Ø:2-4¼ in (5-11 cm). Cap conical or umbonate, then flattening, mouse-gray or slate-colored, shiny and very fibrillose, with typical yellow highlights, sometimes with violet tints. Gills wide, white, or slightly yellowing. Stipe white, tinted lemon yellow in places. Flesh white, sometimes yellowing on the surface. Floury odor and flavor.

HABITAT: Coniferous forests, especially pine, in the lowlands and mountains, but most frequent at altitudes of 1,670 to 3,330 ft (500 to 1,000 m), more rarely under deciduous trees; prefers sandy soil. Appears late, from mid-fall to early winter, and does not fear frost. Uneven distribution, very common in places.

SPECIAL FEATURES

In the regions in which this mushroom is abundant, it is sold to canneries. There are a number of varieties of the species, one of which grows under deciduous trees and is larger.

EDIBILITY

Very good to eat.

TRICHOLOMA PARDINUM, T. TIGRINUM

Tiger Tricholoma

DESCRIPTION: H:2-6 in (5-15 cm), Ø:2¼-7¼ in (6-18 cm).
Cap domed then convex, with a thick, wavy margin, covered in fine gray scales arranged in tiger-stripe pattern, against a pale gray background. Dirty white gills crowded and sinuate. Stipe can be as large as 1½ in (4 cm) in diameter at the base, white or reddening. Flesh thick with floury odor and mild flavor.

POTENTIAL CONFUSION

▶ *TRICHOLOMA TERREUM*
Dirty Tricholoma   EDIBLE

HABITAT: in groups in fir or beech woods, in the mountains on limestone soil. Summer through fall. Common in places.

TOXICITY

Poisonous, causing severe gastro-enteritis.

concentric gray wavy circles

TRICHOLOMA EQUESTRE

Saddle-shaped Tricholoma

DESCRIPTION:
H: 2½-4 in (7-10 cm), Ø:2-4 in (5-10 cm). Hemispherical or conical cap, margin inrolled at first then flattening, with or without an umbo. Surface viscid when wet, yellowish-olive, reddening in the center, covered in scales scattered with red or brownish ocher. Gills bright yellow, crowded,

paler at the upper part. Stipe solid, and bright yellow. Flesh firm, bright yellow, with mild floury odor and flavor.

HABITAT: in groups in lowland or mountain deciduous woods. Fall through early winter in southern regions. Fairly common.

SPECIAL FEATURES

A species is found in pine forests on sandy soil (especially along the southwestern Atlantic coast of Europe) which some mycologist differentiate from *Tricholoma Equestre*. It is called the Golden Tricholoma *(Tricholoma auratum)*. It is larger, the cap being up to 6 in (15 cm) in diameter and the stipe up to 1¼ in (3 cm) wide, with a cap that is more golden or reddish. The stipe is paler yellow and the flesh whitish.

POTENTIAL CONFUSION

▶ *TRICHOLOMA SULPHUREUM*
Sulfur Tricholoma

▶ *AMANITA PHALLOIDES*
Death Cap   DEADLY

EDIBILITY

Very good to eat.

TRICHOLOMA SULPHUREUM
Sulfur Tricholoma

DESCRIPTION: H:2¹/₂-4¹/₂ in (6-12 cm), Ø:1¹/₄-4 in (3-10 cm).
Cap conical or hemispherical, then depressed, sulfur yellow, sometimes shaded with russet, with a depressed or slightly umbonate center. Sulfur yellow gills thick and widely spaced. Stipe thicker at the base, striated with reddish fibrils on a sulfur yellow ground, but white at the base. Flesh thin, also sulfur yellow, with a strong gaseous or sulfurous odor and unpleasant flavor.

HABITAT: deciduous or coniferous woods. On fairly acidic soil, from sea level to mountains. Fall. Very common and widespread.

POTENTIAL CONFUSION
▶ *TRICHOLOMA EQUESTRE*   Saddle Tricholoma   EDIBLE

TRICHOLOMA TERREUM
Dirty Tricholoma

DESCRIPTION: H:1¹/₄-4 in (3-10 cm), Ø:1¹/₂-3¹/₄ in (4-8 cm).
Cap conical at first then more or less flattened , with radial striations, mouse-gray or gray-brown, often umbonate. Gills very wide, white, turning gray. Stipe short and thick, fibrous, slightly spindle-shaped or thickening at the base, solid then hollow, white or dirty white. Flesh firm and thin, whitish, almost odorless, with a pleasant odor becoming bitter with age.

HABITAT: grows in large groups in coniferous woods (pine and spruce), on limestone soil. Fall and even early winter in the south. Common in some places.

EDIBILITY
Good to eat.

POTENTIAL CONFUSION
▶ *TRICHOLOMA PARDINUM*   Tiger Tricholoma   POISONOUS

TRICHOLOMA VIRGATUM

Acrid Tricholoma

DESCRIPTION: H:2³/₄-4 in (7-10 cm), Ø: 1¹/₂-3¹/₄ in (4-8 cm).

SPECIAL FEATURES

The very similar Gray Tricholoma *(Tricholoma scioides),* grows under deciduous trees. It is distinguished mainly by its gills of which the edges are spotted with black. The stipe is thinner at the base, and all parts of the mushroom can become tinted pink.

Cap conical then flattening and umbonate, silver-gray or cinder-gray, with more or less visible grayish or black radiating fibrils or marks, sometimes slightly scaly. Gills pale gray with crenelated edges. Stipe slightly bulbous at the base, whitish and fibrillose. Flesh white or pale gray with a faint odor of radish or of earth and an acrid or peppery flavor.

HABITAT: under conifers or in mixed woods. Fall. Fairly common and widespread.

TRICHOLOMA AESTUANS
Burning Tricholoma

DESCRIPTION: H:2-4 in (5-10 cm), Ø:1$\frac{1}{2}$-3$\frac{1}{4}$ in (4-8 cm).
Cap conical or convex then umbonate, covered in radial fibrils, bright sulfur or lemon yellow, reddish-brown in the center, with an almost white margin. Pale yellow gills with eroded edges. Stipe thickened at the base, bright yellow with reddish-brown fibrils, sometimes splashed with dirty pink at the base. Flesh thin and pale, thickening under the umbo. Faint odor, bitter then acrid flavor.

HABITAT: coniferous forests, especially spruce, in the mountains or cooler zones of the northern hemisphere. Uncommon.

POTENTIAL CONFUSION
▶ *TRICHOLOMA EQUESTRE*   Saddle Tricholoma ___ EDIBLE

TRICHOLOMA ATROSQUAMOSUM
Scaly Tricholoma

DESCRIPTION: H:2$\frac{1}{2}$-4 in (6-10 cm), Ø: 1$\frac{1}{4}$-3$\frac{1}{4}$ in (3-8 cm).
Cap conical or convex, then flattened, often with a central umbo, covered in dark gray scales on a paler background. Gills wide and white with brown or spotted black edges. Stipe solid or hollow, fibrous, pale gray or with black scales, and covered in white mycelium at the base. Flesh whitish, mild flavor and spicy or peppery odor.

EDIBILITY
Good to eat.

HABITAT: deciduous or coniferous woods, . on limestone soil, especially in the mountains. Fairly common.

POTENTIAL CONFUSION

▶ *TRICHOLOMA PARDINUM*
Tiger Tricholoma   POISONOUS

TRICHOLOMA SAPONACEUM

Soap-scented Tricholoma

DESCRIPTION: H:3¹/₄-6 in (8-15 cm), Ø: 2¹/₂-5 in (6-13 cm).
Cap hemispherical then flattened, fleshy, very variable, from gray through gray-green, whitish, brown, and yellowish, sometimes covered in thin scales. Gills widely spaced and brad, white to yellow, sometimes spotted with red. Whitish to dark-gray stipe, sometimes scaly and often shaded pink at the base. Flesh firm and white, reddening at the base of the stipe; strong odor of soap.

HABITAT: solitary or in colonies in deciduous or coniferous woods, in lowland and highland. Summer through fall. Common and widespread.

SPECIAL FEATURES

Very variable mushroom taking on various forms, which differ from each other mainly in the color of the stipe or cap and the presence or absence of scales. All varieties emit a strongly soapy odor.

MELANOLEUCA BREVIPES
Short-stemmed Melanoleuca

Gills crowded, wide, sinuate but decurrent along a narrow strip, pale then grayish. Stipe shorter than the diameter of the cap, often with a thick bulb at the base, of the same color as the cap but striated with fibrils. Flesh thin, fibrous in the stipe, pale but darkening toward the base; no typical odor, mild or slightly bitter flavor.

DESCRIPTION: H:1½-2 in (4-5 cm), Ø:2-4 in (5-10 cm).
Cap convex at first then slightly umbonate or flat, sometimes irregular, even capable of becoming depressed, always with a short, inrolled margin. Surface smooth, mouse-gray to grayish-brown, darker in the center, paling with age as well as in dry weather.

HABITAT: roadsides, forests, lawns, parks. Summer and fall. Fairly common.

MELANOLEUCA VERRUCIPES
Warty-footed Melanoleuca

Cap flattened, slightly depressed, cream or pale gray ocher, with a darker center. Gills tight, sometimes slightly sloping or decurrent, whitish. Stipe thickening toward the base, white, but dotted with black or brown flakes, except at the top. Flesh white, fruity odor and mild flavor.

HABITAT: lawns, meadows, and on bare ground, on grass under deciduous trees or on buried wood. Uncommon.

DESCRIPTION: H:2¾-4½ in (7-12 cm), Ø:2-4 in (5-10 cm).

MELANOLEUCA COGNATA
Distinctive Melanoleuca

DESCRIPTION: H:3¹/₄-6 in (8-15 cm), Ø:2-4 in (5-10 cm).
Cap convex then flattening, with a large umbo, yellow-brown, fawn ocher or copper color. Gills crowded, pale cream or pinkish cream. Stipe thickened or slightly bulbous at the base, paler than the cap. Flesh whitish; no particular odor or flavor, or smelling and tasting of flour.

HABITAT: wooded meadows, edges of forests. Spring through fall. Fairly common in the mountains, rarer in the plains.

SPECIAL FEATURES
Despite its common name, this species is not particularly easy to distinguish from similar species of *Melanoleuca*.

MELANOLEUCA MELALEUCA
Black-and-white Melanoleuca

DESCRIPTION: H:2-4 in (5-10 cm), Ø:2-4 in (5-10 cm).
Cap convex at first, then flattening and becoming slightly depressed in the center, with a central umbo; gray-brown when damp, pale ocher in dry weather. Very crowded white gills, contrasting with darker color of the cap. Stipe gray-brown, with darker longitudinal striations. Flesh white inside the cap, darker toward the base of the stipe. No special odor or flavor.

HABITAT: meadows, roadsides, grassy woods, grass verges. Late summer through fall. Fairly common.

EDIBILITY
Average edibility, flesh soft and very little of it.

LYOPHYLLUM CONNATUM

Tufted Lyophyllum

DESCRIPTION: H:2-4$\frac{1}{2}$ in (5-12 cm),
Ø:1$\frac{1}{2}$-3$\frac{1}{4}$ in (4-8 cm).
Cap stays convex for a long time, then flattening, matte or silky white surface. Tightly packed, white gills, turning cream or pale yellow. Stipe thinner at the base, the same color as the cap. Flesh white, smelling slightly fruity, mild flavor.

HABITAT: grows in tufts, sometimes in large groups on lawns, in well-lit, grassy woods and roadsides. Late summer and fall. Fairly common in uplands.

LYOPHYLLUM DECASTES, L. AGGREGATUM

Gray-capped Lyophyllum

DESCRIPTION: H:2-6 in (5-15 cm), Ø:2-6 in (5-15 cm).
Cap convex then expanding, may be umbonate, undulating, smooth and shiny, gray or gray-brown, then paler on the margin, striated with whitish fibrils. Gills crowded, dirty white. Stipe is cylindrical, thickening or retracted at the base. The flesh is elastic, white, thick in the center, without a typical flavor or odor.

HABITAT: grows in tufts in deciduous woods, mainly confined to clearings, grass verges, avenues, and parks. Fall. Common in places and widespread.

EDIBILITY

Fairly good to eat.

CALOCYBE GAMBOSA
St George's Mushroom

DESCRIPTION: H:2-4 in (5-10 cm), Ø:1$\frac{1}{2}$-4$\frac{1}{2}$ in (4-12 cm).
Cap remaining hemispherical for a long time, with an inrolled margin, becoming irregular and lumpy, very fleshy, with a surface as smooth and velvety as chamois leather, creamy white, sometimes tinted with rust. Very crowded, emarginate, very narrow gills. Stipe thick, $\frac{1}{2}$ to 1$\frac{1}{4}$ in (1 to 3 cm) in diameter, full, the same color as the cap. Flesh white and firm, very thick at the center of the cap; very strong odor and flavor of flour.

EDIBILITY

Edible and good. Some people consider it to be the best edible mushroom, but for others the strong floury flavor is not appreciated.

HABITAT: grows in groups or circles in meadows and grassy woods, beside hedgerows, especially under hawthorn and blackthorn, and in parks. Favors non-acidic and limestone soil. Spring, especially April and May, sometimes through to early summer. Uncommon in some places, frequent in others, especially on high ground.

POTENTIAL CONFUSION

▶ *ENTOLOMA LIVIDUM*
Livid Entoloma   POISONOUS
▶ *INOCYBE PATOUILLARDII*
Red-staining Inocybe   POISONOUS

very crowded white gills

CALOCYBE CARNEA
Flesh-colored Mushroom

DESCRIPTION: H:1$\frac{1}{4}$-2$\frac{1}{2}$ in (3-6 cm), Ø:$\frac{3}{4}$-1$\frac{1}{2}$ in (2-4 cm).
Cap not very fleshy, convex then flattened, with an inrolled margin, flesh-pink, more or less brown in the center. Gills white, not crowded. Stipe the same color as the cap. Flesh white, faint odor and mild flavor.

HABITAT: in small groups in meadows, on lawns, in parks, and beside forest paths. Fall. Uncommon.

NYCTALIS ASTEROPHORA, ASTEROPHORA LYCOPERDOIDES
Star-bearing Nyctalis

DESCRIPTION: H:$\frac{1}{2}$-1$\frac{1}{4}$ in (1-3 cm), Ø:$\frac{1}{2}$-1$\frac{1}{4}$ in (1-3 cm).
Globose, white cap turning chamois color due to the accumulation of a thick layer of spores, which are deposited on the cap when the fungus matures. Gills white, reduced to widely spaced thick folds, sometimes absent. Stipe short and wavy, white. Flesh thick and whitish, rancid odor.

HABITAT: often in groups or tufts growing on Blackening Russula *(Russula nigricans)* and more rarely on other Russulas, which it causes to rot. Summer and fall, especially after heavy rain. Fairly common.

THE TRICHOLOMATALES

NYCTALIS PARASITICA
Parasitic Nyctalis

DESCRIPTION: Ø:¹/₂-1¹/₄ in (1-3 cm).
Cap hemispherical or conical then flattened
and umbonate; surface silky, smooth or striated, dirty white, turning gray. Gills thick and
widely spaced, pale gray. Stipe thin and
white, about ³/₄ to 1¹/₂ in (2 to 4 cm) long.
Flesh thin, whitish; strong, rather unpleasant
odor, mild flavor.

HABITAT: parasitizes certain rotting speci-
mens of Russula, such as the Blackening
Russula, sometimes found on Milk Caps.
Fall. Uncommon.

OUDEMANSIELLA MUCIDA
Porcelain Mushroom

DESCRIPTION: H:1¹/₄-4 in (3-10 cm), Ø:
1¹/₄-3¹/₄ in (3-8 cm).
Cap hemispherical then convex, brilliant
white or slightly russet with age, especially
in the center, covered with a thick mucus.
Gills widely spaced, wide, and white. Stipe
thick or bulbous toward the base, striated
above the ring, smooth and viscid below.
The well-developed ring is situated quite
high on the stipe. Flesh thin and white, with
a pleasant odor and flavor.

HABITAT: in groups or clumps on recent
wounds in the trunks and branches of beech
trees. From late summer through late fall.
Very common.

OUDEMANSIELLA RADICATA
Rooting Shank

DESCRIPTION: H:4-8 in (10-20 cm), Ø:1½-4 in (4-10 cm).
Cap convex but soon flattening, with a central umbo; viscid, smooth then very wrinkled, ocher, russet, or hazelnut. Gills wide and white. Stipe white at the top, the same color as the cap toward the bottom, not viscid, but coriaceous and very long, often twisted, thickening at the base and extended downward by a rhi-zomorph running deep into the soil. Flesh soft, thin, and white; faint odor, mild or slightly bitter flavor.

HABITAT: on tree trunks and stumps of deciduous trees, especially beech. Summer through fall. Common and widespread.

CYSTODERMA AMIANTHINUM
Saffron Parasol

DESCRIPTION: H:1¼-2¾ in (3-7 cm), Ø:¾-1½ in (2-4 cm).
Cap conical then flattening and umbonate, yellow-orange through fawn, granulose or powdery, wrinkled in the center, with a fringed, velvety margin. Gills crowded and wide, white then pale yellow. Stipe hollow, smooth at the top, elsewhere covered in granulations or red flakes, up to the scaly ring which is often poorly defined. Flesh thin, orange-yellow; unpleasant odor, mild flavor.

HABITAT: on the ground in deciduous or coniferous woods, on rather acidic soil. Late summer and fall. Common.

FLAMMULINA VELUTIPES
Velvet Shank

bright orange, slimy cap

velvety, brownish-black stipe

DESCRIPTION: H:1$\frac{1}{2}$-4 in (4-10 cm), Ø:1$\frac{1}{4}$-4 in (3-10 cm).
Cap convex then flattened and becoming undulating, orange to reddish, often reddish-orange on the margin and reddish to reddish-brown in the center, smooth, viscid when wet. Gills white and wide, then pale orange-yellow, dotted with rust as the fungus ages. Stipe often curved, soon becoming hollow, coriaceous, yellow at first then turning brown or black from the bottom, and covered in the characteristic thick, velvety coat. Flesh soft and white, pleasant odor and mild flavor.

HABITAT: growing in clumps, occasionally alone, on tree stumps, dead wood, wounds in living trees, or on the roots of deciduous trees, as well as on broom. Late fall and winter, frost-resistant. Common.

SPECIAL FEATURES

In Japan, the Velvet Shank is cultivated on a large scale. The Japanese produce several tens of thousands of tons of it a year. The mushroom is not popular in the West, but is occasionally eaten in eastern Europe.

EDIBILITY

Quite good to eat, but the flesh is gelatinous or rubbery. The fibrous stipe should be discarded, as should the slimy cuticle.

MARASMIUS ALLIACEUS

Garlic-scented Marasmius

DESCRIPTION: H:4-6 in (10-15 cm), Ø:³/₄-1¹/₂ in (2-4 cm).
Cap cream through brown, sometimes fawn through ocher, remaining convex for a long time. Margin has long striations when wet. Gills white. Stipe very long (up to 8 in (20 cm)) and slender, thickening at the base, hollow but rigid, brownish-black, paler at the top, pruinose and felted with mycelium at the base, often rooting deep into the soil. Strong smell and garlic flavor.

HABITAT: solitary, on leaves and rotting litter in beech woods, on limestone soil. Summer through fall. Uncommon.

EDIBILITY

Not edible, except as a condiment.

MARASMIUS ANDROSACEUS

Horsehair Mushroom

DESCRIPTION: H:1¹/₄-2¹/₂ in (3-6 cm), Ø:¹/₄-¹/₂ in (0.5-1 cm).
Tiny cap, soon flattening, sectioned like a parachute, sometimes depressed in the center, reddish-pink or brown. Gills very widely spaced, the same color as the cap. Thread-like stem, very rigid, blackish and shiny, like horsehair. Very thin, odorless flesh, and mild flavor.

HABITAT: in groups on plant debris on the ground, especially pine-needles, leaves, or twigs. Spring through fall. Fairly common.

SPECIAL FEATURES

Many species of Marasmius grow on woody debris, but due to their small size, they often pass unnoticed.

MARASMIUS OREADES
Fairy Ring Champignon

DESCRIPTION: H:1¹/₄-4 in (3-10 cm), Ø:³/₄-2³/₄ in (2-7 cm).

Cap conical or campanulate at first, then flattening out, becoming undulating and slightly striated on the margin; center always raised into a large umbo. Reddish-ocher when waterlogged, creamy white when dry. Gills wide, wide apart and separating further as the cap expands. Cream or pale grayish-white, taking on a color similar to that of the cap. Stipe thin, fibrous, and firm but remarkably elastic, smooth, sometimes twisted, becoming hollow with age, pale at the top and reddish toward the base, deeply anchored in the soil. Flesh thick in the center, whitish; odor reminiscent of bitter almonds, mild flavor.

HABITAT: meadows, pastures, lawns, roadsides, golf courses and any grassy plot; often forms circles or lines, on any type of soil. Spring through fall. Very common.

POTENTIAL CONFUSION

▶ **MARASMIUS COLLINUS**
Hill Marasmius   POISONOUS
▶ **CLITOCYBE DEALBATA, C. RIVULOSA**
White Clitocybe species POISONOUS

SPECIAL FEATURES

The stipe of the Fairy Ring Mushroom is extraordinary elastic and can be wound round several times around itself without it breaking.

EDIBILITY

Very good to eat; the coriaceous stipe should be discarded.

MARASMIUS RAMEALIS
Branch-gilled Fungus

DESCRIPTION: H: $\frac{1}{2}$-1$\frac{1}{4}$ in (1-3 cm), Ø: $\frac{1}{4}$-$\frac{5}{8}$ in (0.5-1.5 cm).
Cap convex then flattened, slightly wrinkled, cream through pinkish-white, or redder. Gills of the same color. Stipe short, no longer than 1$\frac{1}{4}$ in (3 cm) and $\frac{1}{2}$ in (1 cm) wide, elastic, whitish at the top, reddish and spotted with white fibers at the base. Flesh white, odorless and flavorless.

HABITAT: in large groups on branches and dead twigs and stems of bramble bushes. Summer through fall. Common.

MARASMIUS ROTULA
Little Wheel Fungus

DESCRIPTION: H:1$\frac{1}{4}$-2 in (3-5 cm), Ø:$\frac{3}{8}$-$\frac{5}{8}$ in (0.8-1.5 cm).
Hemispherical or convex cap, in the form of a parachute, typically furrowed, with a dentate margin, always with a well-marked central depression. Ivory, sometimes ocher or gray Gills cream, wide apart, not attached to the stipe but to a membrane encircling the top of the stipe. Stipe

long and very slender, rigid, black or dark brown, whitish at the top. Flesh white in the cap, brown in the stipe, with a faint odor and flavor.

HABITAT: in dense clumps on fallen twigs and branches of deciduous trees. Late spring through to early winter. Very common.

CRINIPELLIS STIPITARIUS
Hairy Marasmius

DESCRIPTION: H:³/₄-1¹/₂ in (2-4 cm), Ø:¹/₂-³/₄ in (1-2 cm).
Cap convex or slightly depressed, sometimes with a tiny umbo, covered in reddish-brown silky hairs on a pale background. Gills pale. The stipe is short, sometimes wider at the top, rigid, undulating, often furrowed, russet and covered in tiny, stiff hairs.

HABITAT: grows on dry twigs, thatch, poor grassland and grassy moors, in summer through fall. Fairly common and widespread.

STROBILURUS ESCULENTUS
Edible Tough-shank

DESCRIPTION: H:³/₄-2 in (2-5 cm), Ø:¹/₄-1¹/₄ in (0.5-3 cm).
Cap convex then flattening, ocher or reddish-brown viscid, sometimes slightly creased. Gills white, turning gray, fairly crowded. Stipe thin, coriaceous, and smooth, often undulating, orange or brown, paler toward the top, with white filaments at the base. Flesh white, thin, rather coriaceous. Faint odor, fungal flavor.

HABITAT: in groups, on spruce cones that have fallen or are buried beneath moss, sometimes on fir cones. From late winter through early spring. Fairly common.

EDIBILITY

Despite its name, this Tough-shank is not particularly tasty, and it is extremely small. Its interest lies in the fact that it appears at a time of year when other mushrooms are rare.

STROBILURUS TENACELLUS
Tenacious Tough-shank

with paler or redder center. Gills white, contrasting with darker color of the cap. Stipe smooth, rooting, white or yellow at first, then taking on the color of the cap from the base, passing through orange-brown. Flesh white and very thin; faint odor and bitter flavor.

DESCRIPTION: H:$^3/_4$-2$^1/_2$ in (2-6 cm), Ø:$^1/_2$-1 in (1-2.5 cm).
Cap smooth, reddish brown or date-brown,

HABITAT: on Scots pine cones, which may be buried in the soil, sometimes on other cones. Spring. Fairly common.

BAEOSPORA MYOSURA
Mouse-tail Tough-shank

DESCRIPTION : H:$^3/_4$-1$^1/_2$ in (2-4 cm), Ø:$^1/_2$-1$^1/_4$ in (1-3 cm).
Cap convex then flat, sometimes with small umbo; smooth, beige, ocher, pinkish brown or hazelnut, paler at the margin. Gills very

crowded, white or beige. Stipe the same color as the cap, downy, ending in a long rhizomorph covered in white hairs which digs deep into the substrate. Flesh thin and beige; fungal odor, mild flavor.

HABITAT: on pine or spruce cones, fallen on the ground or buried, or on their detached scales, in forests and parks. From fall through early winter. Probably common but often unnoticed.

SPECIAL FEATURES

Many species grow on fallen pine cones. These include the *Strobilurus* and some species of Mycena and Collybia. They can be identified mainly through their microscopic characteristics.

MICROMPHALE PERFORANS
Perforating Marasmius

DESCRIPTION: H:⁵/₈-1¹/₄ in (1.5-3 cm), Ø:¹/₄-⁵/₈ in (0.5- 1.5 cm).
Cap convex to flattened, beige to pinkish-brown, with a furrowed margin and center more or less depressed. Gills beige to pinkish-brown. Stipe barely ¹/₃₂ in (1 mm) in diameter, velvety and blackish, except at the top, where it is paler. The flesh has a fetid odor.

HABITAT: often in dense colonies on spruce or fir needles. Summer through fall. Common.

XEROMPHALINA CAMPANELLA
Bell Omphalia

DESCRIPTION: H:³/₄-2 in (2-5 cm), Ø:¹/₂-³/₄ in (1-2 cm).
Cap umbilical from the start, with incurved margin, smooth, slightly viscid, striated up to the umbilicus, orange to reddish-brown. Gills bowed and very decurrent, widely spaced and with some intervening, pale yellow to ochraceous orange. Stipe coriaceous, yellowish-orange at the top, reddish-brown toward the base with stiff, fawn hairs. Flesh thin and coriaceous, reddish-brown, odorless, mild flavor turning slightly bitter.

HABITAT: in dense clusters, sometimes attached at the base of the stipe, mainly on the rotten stumps and branches of conifers, on high ground. Spring through fall. Fairly common to rare.

MEGACOLLYBIA PLATYPHYLLA
Shredded Tough-shank

DESCRIPTION: H:2³/₄-5 in (7-13 cm), Ø:2-4 in (5-10 cm).
Cap hemispherical or campanulate at first, often umbonate, soon flattening, sometimes depressed in the center, gray or gray-brown covered in dark-gray radial fibrils; when older and in dry weather, the surface cracks and shreds, showing the white flesh underneath. Gills very wide, white then pale ocher. Stipe thickening toward the

mycelial cords

base, very fibrous, slightly paler than the cap, extended at the base by very long, thick, brittle, whitish, cottony mycelial cords. Flesh brittle, white and coriaceous, mild or slightly bitter flavor.

HABITAT: on half-buried plant matter, near deciduous trees or stumps. Spring through fall. Very common.

COLLYBIA BUTYRACEA
Buttery Tough-shank

DESCRIPTION: H:2-4 in (5-10 cm), Ø:1¹/₂-3¹/₄ in (4-8 cm).
Cap domed then convex, with a large umbo, reddish brown or graying depending on the variety, becoming markedly paler when dry, margin often paler than the rest of the cap,

and with a darker umbo; typically smooth surface which feels greasy or buttery to the touch. Gills crowded and white. Stipe gradually expanding toward the base into a spongy, very fibrous bulb, which becomes hollow and is similar in color to the cap. Pleasant odor and mild flavor.

HABITAT: deciduous or coniferous forests on acidic soil. From fall through early winter. Very common and widespread.

COLLYBIA CONFLUENS

Clustered Tough-shank

DESCRIPTION: H:2$^1/_2$-4 in (6-10 cm), Ø:$^3/_4$-1$^1/_2$ in (2-4 cm).
Cap convex then flattening, whitish, yellowish or gray-beige. Gills very crowded, the same color as the cap. Stipe long and thin, the same color as the cap at first, compressed, sometimes with a central furrow along its length., becoming darker and reddish-brown, and covered with a fine whitish down. Flesh coriaceous and thin; pleasant odor and flavor.

HABITAT: in dense tufts on pine-needles or leaves, often in lines or rings, on acidic soil. Late summer and fall. Common.

*cap conical
or campanulate*

*stipe white, spotted
with rust*

COLLYBIA DISTORTA

Twisted Tough-shank

DESCRIPTION: H:2^1/$_2$-4^1/$_2$ in (6-12 cm), Ø: 1^1/$_2$-3^1/$_4$ in (4-8 cm).
Cap conical or campanulate, then convex and umbonate, smooth, bright reddish-brown, margin inrolled for a long time, becoming very undulating. Gills very crowded, white, reddening. Stipe white , splashed with rust, covered in longitudinal striations in a broad spiral pattern, giving a twisting impression. Pleasant odor and mild flavor.

HABITAT: in small groups in coniferous woods, sometimes among deciduous trees, on the ground or on rotten buried branches In summer and fall. Fairly common.

COLLYBIA DRYOPHILA

Oak Tough-shank

DESCRIPTION: H:1^1/$_2$-2^3/$_4$ in (4-7 cm), Ø:1^1/$_4$-2 in (3-5 cm).
Cap convex then flattening and sinuous, smooth, yellow-brown to russet, with a paler margin and faint striations, turning almost white in dry weather. Gills crowded and white. Stipe hollow, very fibrous, same color as the cap or orange-brown, paler toward the top, hairy base embedded in the leaf litter. Faint odor, mild flavor.

very smooth cap

HABITAT: often in large groups on the forest floor amid deciduous or coniferous trees. Spring through early winter. Very common.

COLLYBIA FUSIPES

Spindle-shank

DESCRIPTION: H:2³/₄-7 in (7-18 cm), Ø: 1¹/₂-3¹/₄ in (4-8 cm).
Cap convex, then flattening, and rounded, sometimes with a large umbo; smooth, reddish brown with darker splashes of color, turning paler with age. Gills widely spaced, whitish then reddening. Stipe spindle-shaped, flattened and deeply furrowed, very coriaceous and elastic, the same color

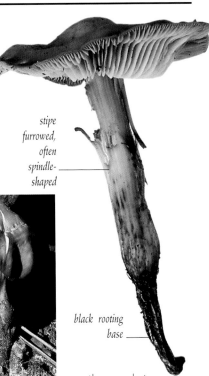

stipe furrowed, often spindle-shaped

black rooting base

as the cap but paler at the top; all the stipes in a single tuft are fused together into a sort of blackish-brown rhizomorph which is buried deep in the substrate. Flesh coriaceous and whitish, odorless or slightly rancid, mild flavor.

HABITAT: in dense tufts on tree-trunks or stumps of deciduous trees, especially oak and beech. Summer through fall. Common.

TOXICITY

Formerly considered edible when young, this mushroom has already caused stomach upsets, perhaps due to the consumption of specimens that were too old. The symptoms can persist for several weeks.

COLLYBIA KUEHNERIANA
Red-stemmed Tough-shank

DESCRIPTION: H:1½-2¾ in (4-7 cm), Ø:¾-2 in (2-5 cm).
Cap convex then flattening, often with an undulating margin; beige to pale russet. When the cap is damp, the gills show through the transparent cuticle, which wrinkles in dry weather. Gills whitish or beige. Dark red stipe paler at the top, very thin and long, cylindrical, sometimes thicker at the top, compressed, and may have a longitudinal furrow. Hairy at the base. Pleasant odor.

HABITAT: singly or in clumps on the rotting stumps and buried branches of deciduous trees. Fall. Fairly common.

COLLYBIA MACULATA
Spotted Tough-shank

DESCRIPTION: H:2¾-5½ in (7-14 cm), Ø:1½-4 in (4-10 cm).
Cap hemispherical at first then convex, smooth and completely matte white at first but soon spotted with rust-red patches. Gills thin and very crowded, cream, finely sinuate. Stipe long, very tough and fibrous, more or less rooting, creamy white like the cap, but may be spotted with rust toward the base. Flesh white, thick in the center, coriaceous, and bitter-tasting after a few seconds.

HABITAT: in groups or tufts, rings or lines in coniferous forests, mainly pines, or in mixed forests on acid soil. Late summer through fall. Fairly common.

COLLYBIA PERONATA
Wood woolly-foot

DESCRIPTION: H:2-3¼ in (5-8 cm), Ø: 1¼-2½ in (3-6 cm).
Cap convex then flattening , with a small umbo which becomes wrinkled with age, ocher, fawn, or brown. Gills widely spaced, yellowish at first, then cinnamon. Stipe thin, but thickening toward the base, covered in long whitish or yellow hairs over one third of the lower part. Flesh coriaceous; odor of vinegar when rubbed, very peppery flavor, which burns the tongue in a few seconds.

HABITAT: in small groups on damp leaf-litter in deciduous woods, especially beech, or conifers. From late summer through fall. Very common.

detachable viscid cuticle on the cap

MYCENA EPIPTERYGIA
Fern Mycena

DESCRIPTION: H:1½-3¼ in (4-8 cm), Ø:½-¾ in (1-2 cm).
Cap conical or convex, striated almost to the center, with a denticulate margin, ocher or cream, covered with a detachable gelatinous layer. Gills pale in color. Stipe long and slender, ¹⁄₁₆ in (2 mm) wide at most, viscid, bright yellow at the top. The base is sometimes discolored or reddish. Flesh very thin, yellowish, with faint odor and mild flavor.

HABITAT: in colonies on moss or leaves in deciduous or coniferous forests, where the soil is acidic and damp. Summer through fall. Common and widespread.

top of stipe yellow.

MYCENA CROCATA

Orange Milk Mycena

DESCRIPTION: H:2³/₄-4¹/₄ in (7-11 cm), Ø:¹/₂-1¹/₄ in (1-3 cm).
Cap conical then convex and umbonate, striated over the whole diameter, whitish or grayish, spotted with orange. Gills the same color. Stipe brownish-orange, paler or yellow at the top, covered in white or yellowish filaments at the base. Flesh thin, saffron yellow, exuding an orange-colored milk when stem or cap are broken. Odorless with a mild flavor.

HABITAT: on leaf-litter especially of beech. Fairly common, in certain places.

carrot-colored patches

MYCENA SANGUINOLENTA
Red-milk Mycena

DESCRIPTION: H:2-3$\frac{1}{4}$ in (5-8 cm),
Ø:$\frac{1}{2}$ in (1 cm).
Cap conical, sometimes flattening with a central umbo, reddish-brown or pinkish-brown, darker in the center, striated or transparent, the gills showing through the cap. Gills widely spaced, pale with pale brown edges. Stipe very long and very slender, the same color or darker than the cap. When broken a little pale red or pink milk is exuded. Flesh very thin and reddish, faint odor and mild flavor.

HABITAT: on moss or leaves in deciduous or coniferous forests. Summer through fall. Very common.

MYCENA HAEMATOPUS
Bleeding Mycena

DESCRIPTION: H:2-4$\frac{1}{2}$ in (5-12 cm), Ø:$\frac{3}{4}$-1$\frac{1}{4}$ in (2-3 cm).
Cap conical or campanulate, striated to the middle in damp weather, pink or pink ocher and powdery. Gills pinkish-white, the same color as the cap. Stipe exudes a blood-red

SPECIAL FEATURES

These two mycenas *(Mycena sanguinolenta)*, are the only fungi which exude a red milk. *Mycena crocata* exudes an orange milk.

milk when broken. Flesh blood-red, no typical odor and mild or slightly bitter flavor.

HABITAT: in tufts on the stumps of deciduous trees. Summer and fall. Fairly common to uncommon. Widespread.

MYCENA INCLINATA
Inclined Mycena

DESCRIPTION: H:$3^1/_4$-$4^1/_2$ in (8-12 cm), Ø: $^3/_4$-$1^1/_2$ in (2-4 cm).
Cap campanulate, with a strongly striated margin to the middle of the cap, and a toothed edge, gray brown but darker in the center. Gills cream-colored then flesh-colored. Stipe often curved, hollow and brittle, white at first, then clearly reddening from the base, finally reddish-brown and whitish at the top. Flesh thin, smelling strongly of grease. Mild flavor.

HABITAT: in dense tufts on old deciduous tree stumps, mainly oak and chestnut. Fall and early winter. Very common and widespread.

MYCENA GALOPUS
Milk-drop Mycena

DESCRIPTION: H:2-4 in (5-10 cm), Ø:$^3/_4$-$1^1/_4$ in (2-3 cm).
Cap hemispherical or conical, often downy, striated over almost all the surface, beige through gray-brown, darker in the center. Gills widely spaced, white to gray. Stipe very slender (about $^1/_{16}$ in (2 mm)), smooth and hollow, the base covered in grayish down, and exuding a white latex when broken, which is abundant in young specimens. Flesh thin and white, without any particular odor or flavor.

HABITAT: on woody debris in deciduous or coniferous forests. Summer and fall, until the beginning of winter. Very common and widespread.

SPECIAL FEATURES

This very common mushroom has a white variety called *alba* or *candida* and a black one called *nigra*,considered by some to be a separate species, *Mycena leucogala.*

MYCENA GALERICULATA
Helmeted Mycena

DESCRIPTION: H:3$\frac{1}{4}$-4$\frac{1}{2}$ in (8-12 cm), Ø:1$\frac{1}{4}$-2$\frac{3}{4}$ in (3-7 cm). Cap conical at first then shaped like a pith-helmet, striped up to the umbo, gray-beige through gray-brown. Gills whitish, may turn pink in older specimens. Stipe very coriaceous and hollow, the same color as the cap but paler at the top. Roots into the substrate by means of a rhizomorph. Flesh white and thin with a floury odor and flavor.

HABITAT: grows in clumps or groups on rotting stumps or branches of deciduous trees. In summer and fall. Very common and widespread.

SPECIAL FEATURES

Although one of the largest mycenas in the temperate zone, it is rarely larger than 2$\frac{1}{2}$ in (6 cm) in diameter.

MYCENA POLYGRAMMA
Striped Stem Mycena

DESCRIPTION: H:2-6 in (5-15 cm), Ø:$\frac{3}{4}$-2$\frac{1}{2}$ in (2-6 cm). Cap conical then slightly flattened with a central umbo, wrinkled or deeply striated, gray-brown with a pruinose surface. Gills white or pale gray then turning pink. Stipe amy attain 8 in (20 cm) in length but is a fraction of an inch thick. Silvery-gray and heavily striated along its length, hairy at the base. Flesh whitish at the base. Flesh whitish, odorless, flavor mild.

HABITAT: in small tufts on buried dead wood, old stumps or tree-trunks. In summer and fall, and late in the year. Common and widespread.

MYCENA METATA
Conical Mycena

DESCRIPTION: H: 1¼-2½ in (3-6 cm), Ø:½-1 in (1-2.5 cm). Cap conical, faintly striated along three-quarter of the pruinose area, beige to pale brown with a paler margin tinted yellow or pink. Gills whitish, with reflections turning pink with age. Stipe long and slender, smooth and brown, hairy at the base. Flesh thin, smelling of iodine, the smell becoming stronger when the fungus is dessicated. Mild flavor.

HABITAT: in troops on leaf litter or pine needles. Late summer through late fall. Fairly common.

SPECIAL FEATURES

Another species of Mycena, *Mycena filopes* (= *M. iodolens*) which is just as fragile, possesses this same odor of iodine. The species are often confused, as it is hard to distinguish between them.

MYCENA LEPTOCEPHALA
Thin-capped Mycena

DESCRIPTION: H:1¼-2¾ in (3-7 cm), Ø:½-¾ in (1-2 cm).
Cap ovoïde then campanulate, striated to the center, grayish. Gills pale gray with white edges. Stipe long and thin, thickening slightly at the base, covered in long, white filaments. Flesh very thin, pale in color, smelling of bleach, and with a mild flavor.

HABITAT: grows singly or in groups, but without forming clumps, in coniferous or deciduous forests. Summer through fall. Very common and widespread.

MYCENA VITILIS, M. FILOPES

Strong-stemmed Mycena

DESCRIPTION:
H:2½-5 in (6-13 cm), Ø: ⅝-1¼ in (1.5-3 cm). Convex or conical cap, sometimes umbonate, with a slightly viscid surface and faintly striated or smooth, so thin that the gills can be seen through it. Dirty yellow in color, paler at the margin. Gills broad, whitish then pale gray. Stipe very long and slender (about ¹⁄₁₆ in (2 mm) in diameter), hollow but very rigid and brittle, white or gray-beige, slightly viscid when wet. Flesh thin and pale; no particular odor or flavor.

HABITAT: under deciduous trees, on the ground or on twigs, usually isolated. Summer and fall. Common and widespread.

SPECIAL FEATURES

This fungus is similar to the Striped Stem Mycena *(Mycena polygramma),* and it shares the same habitat, but there are no stripes on its stem.

MYCENA OLIVACEOMARGINATA
Olive-edged Mycena

DESCRIPTION: H:2-2³/₄ in (5-7 cm), Ø:¹/₂-1¹/₄ in (1-3 cm).
Cap conical or campanulate, then expanding, with furrowed margin, the color of oat straw (light brownish-yellow). Gills fairly widely spaced, whitish with an olive-colored edge. Stipe ¹/₈ in (3 mm) thick at most, also yellowish-brown, paler at the top. Flesh very thin, light or dark odor of radish and mild flavor.

HABITAT: lawns and pastures. Summer through fall. Fairly common.

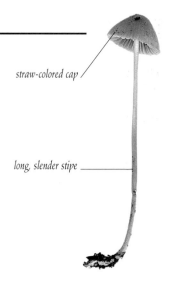

straw-colored cap

long, slender stipe

MYCENA SEYNESII
De Seynes Mycena

DESCRIPTION: H:1¹/₂-3¹/₄ in (4-8 cm), Ø:¹/₂-1¹/₄ in (1-3 cm).
Cap campanulate then expanding, striated margin, pinkish brown to brownish violet. Gills pale pink with a brown edge. Stipe slender, the base curved base covered with a white down and ending in a bulb.

HABITAT: only grows on pine cones, especially on cluster- or sea-pine. Uncommon.

MYCENA PURA
Pure Mycena

DESCRIPTION: H:1¼-3½ in (3-9 cm), Ø: 1¼-1½ in (3-4 cm).

Cap convex then flattening, margin striated in wet weather, pinkish-violet or pinkish and typical in shape but can adopt a variety of colors from white through brown and yellow. Stipe smooth, rigid, hollow and brittle, pinkish-violet or lilac, with whitish hairs or down at the base. Flesh smelling quite strongly of radish.

pinkish-violet cap

pinkish-violet stipe

HABITAT: often grows in groups on leaves in deciduous woods, especially beech, sometimes under conifers. Summer through fall. Common and widespread.

TOXICITY
Poisonous.

SPECIAL FEATURES
There are several varieties of the Pure Mycena, some of which are considered to be separate species. The commonest is the Pink Mycena *(Mycena rosea)* which is larger (the cap can attain 2¼ in (6 cm) in diameter) and which is a uniform bright pink color.

THE AGARICALES

PSATHYRELLA CONOPILUS

Cone-capped Agaric

DESCRIPTION: H:4-6 in (10-15 cm), Ø: (2-4cm).
Conical or campanulate cap, smooth with a striated margin, reddish-brown (date-brown), tending toward grayish ocher as it dries, finely striated or dotted with black when seen under a magnifying-glass. Brown gills with reddish reflections and white edges. Stipe hollow and brittle, straight, can grow up to 8 in (20 cm) long, thicker at the base, smooth and whitish, sprinkled with white at the top. Flesh thin, odorless, mild flavor.

HABITAT: on buried plant debris, disturbed ground, in light copses, at the edge of woods, in parks and gardens. Late summer through fall. Fairly common and widespread.

PSATHYRELLA CANDOLLEANA
Crumble Tuft

DESCRIPTION: H:$1^1/_2$-4 in (4-10 cm), Ø:$1^1/_4$-$3^1/_4$ in (3-8 cm).
Conical cap, then becoming convex, orange yellow or ocher, matte, soon turning pale in dry weather and becoming cream with a darker center and fringed margin, splitting at the end. The gills are broad and very crowded, pinkish-white but soon darkening in stages to lilac brown or violet brown. Stipe smooth and white, soon becoming hollow and fragile. Flesh thin, grayish, with a pleasant odor and mild flavor.

cap almost white in dry weather

HABITAT: singly or more frequently in tufts on rotten wood or near old stumps, in parks, forest paths, and grassy clearings. Spring through fall. Common and widespread.

EDIBILITY

Edible but of no interest because the flesh is too thin.

PSATHYRELLA LACRYMABUNDA

Weeping Widow

DESCRIPTION: H:2¹/₂-4¹/₂ in (6-12 cm),
Ø:1¹/₂-4¹/₂ in (4-12 cm).
Cap domed or conical, then convex, fawn or
russet, covered in woolly fibers. Filaments,
the remains of a veil which covers the gills
in young specimens, hang from the margin.
Gills brown, exuding copious "tears" of
transparent liquid when young, turning gray
in stages, and finally blackening. Stipe fragile, fibrillose, whitish, russet at the base,

turning black at maturity due to being
covered in spores.

HABITAT: singly or in small tufts at roadsides, on forest paths, in gardens and
meadows. Late summer through fall.
Fairly common.

EDIBILITY
Edible when young.

PSATHYRELLA MULTIPEDATA

Clumped Agaric

DESCRIPTION:
H: 3¹/₄-6 in (8-15 cm),
Ø: ¹/₂-1¹/₂ in (1-4 cm).
Conical then
campanulate
cap with a
silky, fibrillose
surface, reddish-brown or
grayish-brown, paling to
ocher as it dries. Gills crowded,
gray-beige, then dark violet brown,
with white edge. Stipe long and
slender, hollow and brittle, smooth

and silky, white and powdery at
the top. Flesh thin, reddish-
brown through beige, odorless,
mild flavor.

HABITAT: in compact tufts,
comprising dozens of specimens
in grassy woods and parks. Late
summer through fall. Uncommon.

—— *voluminous tufts*

PSATHYRELLA PILULIFORMIS

Satin-stemmed Agaric

DESCRIPTION: H: 2-4¹/₂ in (5-12 cm), Ø: (2-5 cm). Conical then campanulate cap, more or less expanded; the edge of the cap is laced with the white remains of the veil; very hygrophanous, changing from yellow ocher in the dry stage to dark reddish-brown when wet. Both shades may be present on the same cap. Gills crowded, pale, then turning gray-brown and finally dark brown with a white edge. Stipe smooth, hollow, and brittle, whitish then turning brown, colored black by the spores. Flesh thin, brown, paling to beige as it dries; faint odor, mild flavor.

HABITAT: in dense tufts on rotting stumps or in the ground around all types of tree trunk. Summer through fall. Common and widespread.

PSATHYRELLA SPADICEOGRISEA

Gray-brown Psathyrella

DESCRIPTION: H: 2-4 in (5-10 cm), Ø: 1¹/₄-2¹/₂ in (3-6 cm).
Cap conical then convex, with a large umbo, finely striated up to the umbo, especially as it ages; ochraceous-brown, fawn or gray-brown, turning grayish later but paling to ocher or dirty cream when dry. The fairly crowded gills are often slightly decurrent on a little strip and remain pale gray for a long time, then turning dark violent brown. Stipe slightly thickened at the base, soon becoming hollow and brittle, smooth and whitish. Flesh pale, odorless, flavor mild.

HABITAT: on the ground or on rotten wood, on humus, along forest paths, under deciduous trees. Mainly in spring (from April), sometimes in the fall. Fairly common and widespread.

COPRINUS DISSEMINATUS

Fairies' Bonnets

DESCRIPTION: H: ³/₄-2 in (2-5 cm),
Ø: ³/₈-⁵/₈ in (0.8-1.5 cm).
Cap ovoid or campanulate, with finely woolly surface, cream when young, then ocher, light brown, or gray, the center remaining ocher, with a smooth surface, deeply striated to the center. Gills white, blackening, but not deliquescent, with white edge. Stipe hollow and thin, very fragile and white. Hardly any flesh, odorless and flavorless.

HABITAT: in huge, densely-packed clumps on or near stumps and rotting wood. Spring through fall. Very common.

COPRINUS DOMESTICUS

Domesticated Ink-cap

DESCRIPTION: H: 2-4 in (5-10 cm),
Ø: ³/₄-2 in (2-5 cm).
Cap ovoid at first then conical, later expanding and slightly convex, ocher with a reddish center. In young specimens it is covered in dense, whitish granulations, which subsequently disappear except at the top. the surface is then striated or furrowed almost to the center. Gills whitish then dark brown. Stem velvety in young specimens, with a scaly bulb at the bottom which sometimes displays the bright red mycelium. Pale flesh, not very deliquescent, faint smell and mild flavor.

HABITAT: On stumps and cut branches of deciduous trees, and even found in the cellars of houses. Late spring through early fall. Fairly common.

COPRINUS MICACEUS
Glistening Ink-cap

DESCRIPTION:
H: 2-4 in (5-10 cm),
Ø: ³/₄-1¹/₂ in (2-4 cm).
Ovoid then conical cap,
striated almost to the center,
with a saw-toothed edge,
brown through ocher, darker
at the center, and sprin-
kled in young specimens
with shiny specks like
mica. Gills white then
purple-brown, black and
finally deliquescent, with
white edge. Stipe long,

hollow and fragile, brittle,
slightly wider toward the
base, white and silky.
Flesh thin, odorless and
flavorless.

HABITAT: in tufts or
groups on or near
rotting deciduous
wood, stumps, half-buried
branches, in copses and
woods, beside paths.
Spring through fall.
Common.

COPRINUS NIVEUS
Snow White Ink-cap

DESCRIPTION:
H: 2-4 in (5-10 cm),
Ø: ³/₄-2 in (2-5 cm).
Ovoid cap, opening like
an umbrella, ending in an
upturned margin which is
often ragged, pure white
pure and floccose at first,
the flakes tending subse-
quently to disperse,
revealing a pale gray
background. Gills white,
blackening and eventually
deliquescing, with a white

edge. Stipe hollow and
brittle, slightly thickening
at the base, pure white,
also floccose in young
specimens. Flesh thin and
gray; no characteristic
odor or flavor.

HABITAT: singly or in
small groups, on buffalo
chips, cowpats, or horse-
dung, in pastures. From
spring through fall. Fairly
common.

COPRINUS LAGOPUS

Hare's-foot Ink-cap

DESCRIPTION: H:2¹/₂-4¹/₂ in (6-12 cm), Ø: ³/₄-1¹/₂ in (2-4 cm).
Cap cylindrical or ovoid, eventually flat and with an upturned edge, entirely covered with white wooly down which eventually disappears, revealing a mouse-gray background, but persisting in the center when the cap is fully expanded. Gills widely-spaced, narrow, whitish then blackening quickly. Stipe cylindrical, thickening at the base, hollow and brittle, covered like the cap with whitish wooly down which is very dense at first. Flesh white, odorless, flavor mild.

HABITAT: scattered or in groups of several individuals in cool places, under bushes and in grassy places in woodland. Summer through fall. Fairly common and widespread.

COPRINUS PICACEUS

Magpie Mushroom or Magpie Cap

DESCRIPTION: H:4-8 in (10-20 cm), Ø:³/₄-2¹/₂ in (2-6 cm).
Cap ovoid and whitish at first, later campanulate and reddish-brown, sprinkled with white. Gills crowded, free, white then reddening, before turning black, eventually liquifying. Stipe hollow, rigid and brittle, thickening toward the base, white and fibrillose. Flesh thin and grayish, with an unpleasant odor and flavor.

HABITAT: singly or in small groups in deciduous woods, in shady places. Late summer through fall. Uncommon.

TOXICITY
Poisonous.

COPRINUS ATRAMENTARIUS

Common Ink-cap

DESCRIPTION: H:2-6 in (5-15 cm), Ø:1½-2½ in (4-6 cm). Cap ovoid at first, with little brown flakes at the top, then opening into a bell-shape and cracking, cream through mouse-gray, striated almost over the whole surface. Gills very crowded, white, soon blackening starting at the edge and melting into a black liquid. Stipe hollow and brittle, fibrillose, white, marked at the base with a reddish annular zone, deeply embedded in the substrate by means of a rooting base. Flesh thin and white, with faint odor and pleasant flavor.

HABITAT: in large dense clumps, rarely singly, on rotting wood, sometimes in the ground, at the foot of old stumps,

in open ground, such as the edge of woods and roadsides. Spring through fall. Common and widespread.

EDIBILITY

When very young it is edible, but alcohol must not be drunk during the meal or it will interact with coprine, producing symptoms such as heart palpitations, nausea, facial congestion, and even disruptions to vision. These effects may even manifest themselves if alcohol is consumed several days after consumption of the mushroom since the principle breaks down very slowly in the human body. Coprine is even used as a cure for alcoholism.

COPRINUS COMATUS

Shaggy Ink-cap, Lawyer's Wig

DESCRIPTION: H: 4-8 in (10-20 cm), Ø: ³/₄-2³/₄ in (2-7 cm).

In young specimens, is elongated into a sheath surrounding the stipe. It is white and entirely covered in long, upturned scales with beige or reddish tips, except at the top which is clearly defined by a round ocher or reddish patch; it then opens very quickly into a bell and starts to liquefy from the edge, turning into thick black ink. The gills are free, very crowded, white but soon turning pink, then black from the edge of the cap. The stipe is long (sometimes more than 8 in (20 cm)), cylindrical and hollow, slightly bulbous, becoming dirty gray or brown upon maturity; it has a little ring which eventually becomes detached and falls off. The flesh is white and soft, with little, odor or flavor.

EDIBILITY

Very good to eat, even when raw. However, the Shaggy Ink-Cap absolutely must be picked very young, while the gills are still white, or all you will be left with in the pan is an unappetizing thick, black liquid. For the same reason, it must be eaten as soon as possible after picking. Cannot be dried or pickled.

HABITAT: in groups, sometimes of very tightly packed individuals on lawns, wasteland and all types of recently disturbed earth, forest paths, and roadsides. From spring through fall. Very common and widespread.

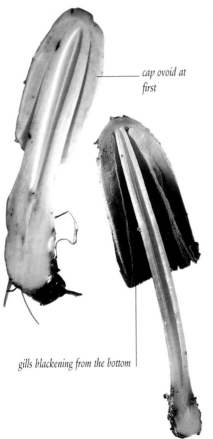

cap ovoid at first

gills blackening from the bottom

SPECIAL FEATURES

It has been possible to grow Shaggy Inkcaps commercially for several years now, either from mycelium or from impregnated compost. However, since there is no method of preserving the fungus, even by freezing, small-scale and large-scale growers of the Cultivated Mushroom and wild mushrooms have been reluctant to produce it.

COPRINUS PLICATILIS
Pleated Ink-cap

DESCRIPTION: H: 1¹/₂-2³/₄ in (4-7 cm), Ø:³/₄-1¹/₄ in (2-3 cm).
The cap is elongated at first into a cylinder or egg-shape, and reddish-brown, but it subsequently expands into a furrowed grayish umbrella, like a parachute, though the center remains smooth and reddish. The gills are white, turning gray but first becoming pinkish. The stipe is very slender and long, hollow and brittle, smooth and white. There is hardly any flesh, and no odor or flavor.

HABITAT: on lawns, in pastures, at roadsides, among grass or on bare soil. Spring through fall. Fairly common.

AGARICUS BITORQUIS
Sidewalk Mushroom

DESCRIPTION: H: 2-4 in (5-10 cm), Ø: 1¹/₂-4 in (4-10 cm).
Cap convex, soon flattening, smooth or fibrillose, white or pale gray, splashed with ocher, often soiled with particles of earth. Gills pale pink then lilac-gray and finally dark brown. Stipe white, full, short and thick, narrowing to a point at the base, with two distinct rings, the lower one wrapping round the stipe like a volva. Flesh thick and and firm turning faintly pink when cut.

HABITAT: on packed earth, even breaking through asphalt, in parks, gardens, footpaths, around trees in cities. In groups, sometimes fused together at the base of the stipe. Summer and autumn. Uncommon.

EDIBILITY
Good to eat.

AGARICUS CAMPESTRIS

Field Mushroom

DESCRIPTION: H: 1½-4 in (4-10 cm), Ø: 1½-4 in (4-10 cm).

Cap thick, globulose or hemispherical at first, becoming almost flat toward the end, smooth and silky, often with white shreds, the remainder of the veil, hanging from the margin, white, slightly yellowing or turning brown, sometimes with small grayish or brownish flattened scales. Gills narrow and crowded, pale pink and gradually darkening to take on a final brownish-black color.

CONFUSION

▶ *AGARICUS XANTHODERMA*
Yellow-staining Mushroom POISONOUS

Stipe short and full, brittle, slightly narrowing but rounded at the base, white, browning with age, fibrillose or slightly floccose beneath the ring. Ring thin and single, not well developed and withering quickly to leave only a slight trace. Flesh white, thick at the center, thin at the edge, turning very slightly pink when cut; pleasant odor and mild flavor.

HABITAT: meadows grazed by cattle, sheep, or horses, from late summer to mid-fall, sometimes in spring; often after showers following a very hot summer. Very common and found all over the world. Grows in groups and may suddenly appear en masse from one day to the next.

EDIBILITY

Very good to eat and can be eaten raw or cooked. The Field Mushroom is best eaten when the cap is "closed," while the gills are still pink.

SPECIAL FEATURES

The common Field Mushroom actually consists of a number of different forms and varieties, which vary mainly in the appearance of the surface of the cap. Some caps are covered in gray, brown, or yellow fibrils or flat scales.

AGARICUS BISPORUS
Cultivated Mushroom

Cap hemispherical at first with a flattened center, becoming depressed with age, and undulating border. Surface smooth and fibrillose, or slightly scaly, especially at the margin, pure white, browning slightly to the touch. Gills crowded and narrow, pale pink, then brown and finally black. Stipe short, (only $1^{1}/_{2}$-$2^{3}/_{4}$ in (4 to 7 cm)), thicker or thinner at the base, white, staining brown when touched ring ascendant (not pendant), faint and fugaceous, striated on the upper surface. Flesh firm and white, turning pink when exposed to the air, especially in the base of the stipe, and browning with age; pleasant odor and mild flavor.

DESCRIPTION: H: 2-4 in (5-10 cm),
Ø: 2-4$^{1}/_{2}$ in (5-12 cm).

EDIBILITY

Excellent eating and can even be eaten raw. The careful selection of wild specimens has contributed to its commercial production. It was first cultivated in France more than 300 years ago in old stone quarries and disused mine workings around Paris, which is why it is known in French as "Champignon de Paris." It is now grown all over the world and although it is the most popular mushroom in the West, the Paddy Straw Mushroom, eaten in southeast Asia, is the most widely cultivated.

HABITAT: manured meadows and gardens, parks, and on old compost. Spring through fall. Not common in the wild but occurring throughout the northern hemisphere.

POTENTIAL CONFUSION

▶ *AGARICUS XANTHODERMA*
Yellow-staining Mushroom POISONOUS

AGARICUS PRAECLARESQUAMOSUS

Scaly Mushroom, Guinea-fowl Mushroom

DESCRIPTION:
H: 2³/₄-5 in (7-13 cm),
Ø: 2¹/₂-4¹/₂ in (6-12 cm).
The cap is covered in dark gray scales on a pale gray background. the Scales are very dense in the center, more widely spaced at the edge, imitating the plumage of the guinea-fowl. Gills crowded, white then pink, and finally blackish-brown. Stipe slightly swollen and bulbous at the base, becoming hollow and brittle; whitish, staining yellow when touched, then brownish. Flesh thick and white, soon turning yellow, especially at the base of the stipe; odor of phenol, mild flavor.

HABITAT: groves, parks, gardens, meadows, the edges of forests. Summer and autumn. Fairly common to uncommon. Appears in large numbers locally.

TOXICITY

Poisonous.

AGARICUS PORPHYRIA

Brown-capped Agaric

DESCRIPTION: H: 2-4 in (5-10 cm),
Ø: 2-3¹/₄ in (5-8 cm).
Cap hemispherical then expanded, with vermillion scales and fibrils on a pinkish background, reddish-brown at the center. Gills crowded, gray-pink, turning dark brown. Stipe thickening into a bulb at the base, pink above the ring, white below it, yellowing at the base. Fragile, white, yellowing ring. Root-like filaments (rhizomorphs) are sometimes visible when the mushroom is uprooted. Flesh white, yellowing mainly around the base of the stipe; odor of bitter almonds.

HABITAT: under deciduous trees, in forests, parks, gardens, and hedgerows. Summer through fall. Uncommon.

EDIBILITY

Good to eat.

AGARICUS AUGUSTUS

Prince Mushroom

DESCRIPTION: H: 4-8 in (10-20 cm),
Ø: 4-8 in (10-20 cm).
Cap globulose or trapezoid, then expanded
or convex, fleshy, with russet or brown
scales on a paler background and shreds of
the veil hanging from the margin. Gills narrow and crowded, remaining pale pinkish-
gray for a long time, then turning purplish-
brown. Stipe thick (up to 1½ in (4 cm))
especially at the base, smooth above the
ring, with white or orange scales below it,
yellowing to the touch; ring large and
white floccose underneath. Flesh white, yel-

lowing in the cap and
reddening in the stipe;
strong odor of bitter
almonds, mild flavor.

HABITAT: deciduous
or coniferous woods,
verges, parks, and grass-
land, sometimes in meadows.
Summer through fall. Fairly
common and widespread.

*dense and fairly
regular russet
scales*

EDIBILITY

Good to eat.

AGARICUS ALBERTII, A. MACROSPORUS

Albert's Mushroom

DESCRIPTION: H: 2³/₄-7 in (7-18 cm), Ø: 3¹/₄-8 in (8-20 cm).
Cap very fleshy, hemispherical at first and up to 12 in (30 cm) in diameter, white, yellowing very slightly, becoming slightly ocher with age, silky or slightly scaly. Gills pinkish-white, turning gray then chocolate brown. Stipe very thick, 1¹/₄ to 2 in (3 to 5 cm) in diameter, slightly swollen in the middle or toward the base, white then splashed with ocher and brown, very downy below the ring, especially in young specimens; ring irregular and downy, floccose underneath in young specimens. Flesh thick, white, yellowing very slightly, turning brown at the base of the stipe. Faint odor of aniseed, becoming an unpleasant ammoniacal odor when old.

HABITAT: in pastures, on lawns, in parks, on non-acidic soil. Summer through early fall. Fairly common to fairly rare.

EDIBILITY

Good to eat, but must be eaten very young. When older, it tends to smell like urine, hence its other name, *Agaricus urinascens*.

AGARICUS SILVATICUS
Brown Wood Mushroom

DESCRIPTION:
H: 2³/₄-5 in (7-13 cm),
Ø: 2-4¹/₂ in (5-12 cm).
Cap conical then flattening,
not very thick, sprinkled with
reddish-brown scales, that are
fairly numerous and widely spaced,
on a whitish background. Gills flesh
pink, turning dark purplish-brown
when mature. Stipe slightly bulbous
and white, becoming hollow and reddening with age; ring membranous
ample and white. Flesh white, quickly
turning red when cut, especially in young
specimens. Pleasant odor and mild flavor.

HABITAT: on the litter of
conifers, especially spruce,
rarer in deciduous woods.
Late summer through
fall. Common. Found all
over the world.

Fairly dense reddish-brown scales

EDIBILITY
Good to eat.

AGARICUS XANTHODERMA
Yellow-staining Mushroom

DESCRIPTION: H: 2³/₄-5 in (7-13 cm),
Ø: 2-4¹/₂ in (5-12 cm).
The cap is trapezoidal in the young specimen, then convex to flattened with a
smooth surface, silky white, becoming bright
yellow when rubbed. The gills are narrow
and crowded, white at first, then turning
grayish-pink then purplish-brown. Stipe
thick or slender and sinuous, with a small

POTENTIAL CONFUSION

All the edible mushrooms, but
especially:
▶ *AGARICUS CAMPESTRIS*
  Field Mushroom   EDIBLE
▶ *AGARICUS ARVENSIS*
  Horse Mushroom   EDIBLE

fused with with the Field Mushroom (*Agaricus campestris*).

SPECIAL FEATURES

The Yellow-staining Mushroom has a fairly characteristic odor of iodine or phenol, and is even more recognizable by the pronounced yellowing of the cap and base of the stipe when touched. The variety described here is the classic type and the most frequently encountered, recognizable by its white color. However, there are other varieties in which the cap is gray, gray-brown, with thin scales, or split into coarser scales. All are equally indigestible.

cap turning chrome yellow when touched

white bulb, turning yellow when rubbed, especially at the bulb; thick, membranous, pendant white ring. The white flesh turns yellow when cut, especially in the bulb; unpleasant odor of iodine, ink, or phenol.

HABITAT: in groups in fertilized meadows, well-lit deciduous or coniferous woods, sand on lawns. Summer through fall. Fairly common.

A slightly different form is found on lawns in North America, which is called the Californian Mushroom (*Agaricus californicus*). The cap is fairly scaly, browning in the center. It is often confused with with the Field Mushroom (*Agaricus campestris*).

TOXICITY

Slightly toxic. The odor, which is unpleasant when the mushroom is picked, becomes foul when it is cooked. Although some people are able to eat this mushroom without the slightest problem, in most people it causes symptoms typical of mild food-poisoning: vomiting, diarrhea, headaches, etc.

AGARICUS ARVENSIS

Horse Mushroom

DESCRIPTION: H: 4-7 in (10-18 cm), Ø: 4-6 in (10-15 cm).
Thick, firm cap, hemispherical then expanding to flat, with a margin that remains inrolled for a long time. Surface smooth, white and satiny, cracking and becoming stained with ocher, yellowing slight to the touch. Gills very crowded, grayish pink, very pale in young specimens, then purplish-brown and finally blackish. Stipe thick (3¼-6 in x ¾-1¼ in (8-15 x 2-3 cm)), especially at the base, becoming hollow with age, white, yellowing to the toucher, slightly floccose in young specimens below the ring. The white ring is membranous and double, the lower one taking the shape of a gear-wheel or star, clearly visible in the young specimen. Flesh thick at the center, white, yellowing slightly, especially in the stipe. Fairly marked odor of aniseed and mild flavor.

HABITAT: pastures, grassy clearings, parks. From late summer to mid-fall, sometimes from the spring. Uncommon to fairly common; widespread, found on every continent.

POTENTIAL CONFUSION	EDIBILITY
▶ *AMANITA PHALLOIDES* Death Cap DEADLY ▶ *AGARICUS XANTHODERMA* Yellow-staining Mushroom POISONOUS	Very good to eat, even when raw. To be eaten young, preferably when the gills are still pale because the spores have not matured yet.

AGARICUS SILVICOLA

Wood Mushroom

fairly bulbous, white or pinkish-violet above the ring, white becoming stained with lemon yellow below it. Ring thin, very full, floccose on the underside. Flesh thick at the center, thin at the edge, white, turning yellow when cut, strong odor of aniseed.

DESCRIPTION: H: 2³/₄-5¹/₂ in (7-14 cm), Ø: 2-4¹/₂ in (5-12 cm).
Cap ovoid or conical, with a flattened then widely expanded top, white to cream, staining yellow when touched, silky or slightly fibrillose. Gills very crowded, pale gray, turning pink and finally sepia. Stipe flexible,

HABITAT: deciduous or coniferous woods. Summer through fall. common.

POTENTIAL CONFUSION

▶ *AMANITA PHALLOIDES*
Death Cap   DEADLY
▶ *AMANITA VERNA*
Spring Amanita   DEADLY
▶ *AMANITA VIROSA*
Destroying Angel   DEADLY

EDIBILITY

Very good to eat, especially when young, even raw.

CYSTOLEPIOTA ASPERA

Pointed-scale Parasol Mushroom

DESCRIPTION:
H: 2³/₄-4¹/₂ in (7- 12 cm),
Ø: 3¹/₄-5 in (8-13 cm).
Cap conical then convex and more or less umbonate, densely covered with conical reddish-brown scales, which are more numerous at the center, showing an ochraceous-gray background in between. Gills broad, very crowded and forked, white then cream. Stipe becoming hollow with age, downy, the same color as the cap, thickening into a small bulb at the base; ring full, pendant, and

membranous, edged with brown flakes. Flesh thin at the edge of the cap, whitish; odor strong and unpleasant; flavor faint but also unpleasant.

HABITAT: found in fertilized soil, such as copses, verges, as well as in deciduous or coniferous woods; prefers nitrogen-rich, limestone soil. Summer through fall. Common and widespread.

TOXICITY
Poisonous.

LEPIOTA CASTANEA
Chestnut Parasol Mushroom

DESCRIPTION: H: 1¹/₂-2¹/₂ in (4-6 cm),
Ø: ³/₄-1¹/₂ in (2-4 cm).
Cap conical at first then flattening and
umbonate, chestnut to russet. Gills white,
slightly reddening. Stipe downy on the lower
half or two-thirds, reddish-brown; ring
absent or faint. Flesh pale ocher, faint odor.

HABITAT: copses and deciduous forests.
Summer through fall. Uncommon.

TOXICITY
Suspected of being poisonous.

LEPIOTA CRISTATA
Stinking Parasol Mushroom

DESCRIPTION: H: 1¹/₄-2¹/₂ in (3- 6 cm),
Ø: ³/₄-2 in (2-5 cm).
Cap conical at first, soon flattening, with a
marked central umbo and margin remaining
inrolled for a long time, sprinkled with reddish-orange concentric scales on a white
background, but uniform red on the umbo.
Gills wide, white, with toothed edges. Stipe
smooth, hollow, and brittle, white or slightly
pink or reddish toward the base, with a

fugaceous white ring. Flesh thin and
whitish; strong, unpleasant odor, flavor mild
but also unpleasant.

HABITAT: in medium to large groups, at
the edge of woods, on lawns, and in well-lit
coniferous or deciduous woods. Summer
through fall. Common and widespread.

TOXICITY
Poisonous.

LEPIOTA IGNIVOLVATA

Red-stemmed Parasol Mushroom

DESCRIPTION: H: 2¹/₂-4¹/₂ in (6-12 cm), Ø: 2-4 in (5-10 cm).
Cap hemispherical and umbonate, then convex and umbonate, reddish ocher or reddish brown at the center; elsewhere the cream background is punctuated with small beige to reddish scales regularly spaced; the margin is long inrolled and fringed (remaining from the hanging veil); The gills are wide and white. The stipe is full then hollow, thickening from top to bottom, with one or two oblique ridges in the center, edged with orange or reddish-brown, and arranged in a ring which is sometimes broken; smooth surface at the top, downy underneath; base turning pink or red with age or from being rubbed (not always noticeable). Flesh white; strong and unpleasant odor, mild but very unpleasant flavor.

HABITAT: conifers or mixed and woods (conifers and deciduous trees), on limestone or neutral soil. Late summer through fall. Fairly common.

ring reddish. oblique

small beige to reddish scales

umbonate cap

LEPIOTA CLYPEOLARIA
Shield-shaped Parasol Mushroom

DESCRIPTION: H: 2¹/₂-5 in (6-13 cm), Ø: 1¹/₂-3¹/₄ in (4-8 cm).
Cap hemispherical at first , then expanding and umbonate, covered in beige or ocher scales on a cream background, paler on the frayed margin. The center is clearly marked by a smooth reddish-brown patch. Gills crowded, white or cream. Stipe swollen toward the base, rigid but hollow and brittle, the lower two thirds are covered in white woolly fibers; ring downy at first, fairly full, but disappearing quite soon.

HABITAT: under deciduous trees (oak, hornbeam) or conifers. Summer through fall. Fairly common.

SPECIAL FEATURES
The Yellowing Shield-shaped Parasol Mushroom *(Lepiota ventriosospora)* is similar but its woolly stem is yellowish.

TOXICITY
Poisonous.

LEPIOTA PSEUDOHELVEOLA
False Brown Parasol Mushroom

DESCRIPTION: H: 2-3¹/₂ in (5-9 cm), Ø: ³/₄-1¹/₄ in (2-3 cm).
Cap conical for a long time, then becoming convex and slightly umbonate, with dark pinkish-brown or sepia scales on a pinkish-white background. Gills white. Stipe long and slender, pinkish-white to pinkish-brown; ring fairly well developed, ridged, whitish, pinkish or grayish brown underneath. Flesh slightly pink, faint odor.

HABITAT: under deciduous trees, especially in warm regions. Summer through fall. Fairly common.

TOXICITY
Poisonous.

LEPIOTA BRUNNEOINCARNATA
Red-brown Parasol Mushroom

DESCRIPTION: H: 1¼-2¾ in (3-7 cm), Ø: 1¼-2¾ in (3-7 cm). Cap convex then expanded, covered in reddish or reddish-brown scales, sometimes very densely, on a pale background tinged with pink, darker brown in the center. Gills crowded, white then slightly yellow. Stipe short (2 in (5 cm) maximum), white at the top, also covered in russet or brown scales on a pink background. Ring quite faint, often a mere ridge on the stipe. The white flesh reddens slightly when cut; mild flavor.

HABITAT: lawns, gardens, verges, grassy woodland, beside hedgerows, on rich soil.

Late summer through fall. Fairly rare, but may be relatively common in certain Mediterranean or Atlantic regions.

TOXICITY
Deadly.

SPECIAL FEATURES

This is one of the group of small brown Parasol Mushrooms once all called *Lepiota helveola*. All these mushrooms are less than 4 in (10 cm) tall, and are colored in shades of pink. Their ring is faint or absent. Care should be taken to distinguish them from the edible Parasol Mushrooms because they can cause serious, and even fatal, poisoning. The main difference is that they are much smaller than the edible species.

LEUCOAGARICUS LEUCOTHITES

The Off-white Parasol

small sliding ring

POTENTIAL CONFUSION

▶ *AMANITA PHALLOIDES*
  Death cap   DEADLY
▶ *AMANITA VERNA*
  Spring Amanita   DEADLY
▶ *AMANITA VIROSA*
  Destroying Angel   DEADLY

DESCRIPTION: H: 2-4 in (5-10 cm), Ø: 2-4 in (5-10 cm).
Cap hemispherical then convex, smooth, white, and silky. Gills remain white for a long time, turning pink or grayish-pink when old. Stipe white, swollen at the base into a small globulose bulb, with an underdeveloped ring, which slides easily up and down the stipe. Flesh white and firm, thick in the cap; no characteristic odor or flavor.

HABITAT: in meadows, parks, gardens, and by roadsides. Summer through fall. Fairly common.

EDIBILITY

Good to eat, but the risk of confusion with the deadly species of Amanita is serious.

SPECIAL FEATURES

This mushroom is one of a complex group containing many species and varieties which are difficult to identify. It is said to be a collective species.

MACROLEPIOTA PROCERA

Parasol Mushroom

DESCRIPTION: H: 6-12 in (15-30 cm) (up to 16 in (40 cm)), Ø: 4-12 in (10-30 cm). Cap ovoid at first, then expanding and eventually flat, but almost always retaining a central umbo; white or cream background entirely covered with grayish scales and brown platelets, reddish-brown or darker brown, fairly well spaced toward the edge, more crowded toward the center and uniformly reddish-brown. The gills are crowded and very thick, free and elastic, remaining white for a long time, eventually darkening to dirty cream. The stipe is longer than the diameter of the cap,

POTENTIAL CONFUSION

▶ *MACROLEPIOTA VENENATA*
Venomous Parasol   POISONOUS

**All the little Parasol Mushrooms
no taller than 4 in (10 cm)
must be avoided, especially:**

▶ *LEPIOTA
BRUNNEOINCARNATA*
Scarlet-brown Parasol   DEADLY

▶ *LEPIOTA CRISTATA*
Crested Lepiota   POISONOUS

▶ *LEPIOTA BRUNNEOLILACINA*
Lilac-brown Parasol   DEADLY

straight, thickening slightly toward the bottom, fibrous and soon becoming hollow, but always rigid. The surface is covered with zigzag striations like a snakeskin, the pattern being larger toward the base. The ring is large and double, very thick and woolly, and can be slid up and down the stipe; the bulb is large and white. The white flesh is thin and soft; faint odor but mild hazelnut flavor.

HABITAT: in small groups in neglected meadows and pastures, fallow land, among heather and bracken, at the edge of woods or hedgerows, and in well-lit deciduous forests. Late summer through fall. Very common and widespread.

brown scaly stripes

SPECIAL FEATURES

The large Parasol Mushrooms is one of the most popular of edible mushrooms, because it is delicious, distinctive and so easy to recognize. Its size means that it can be spotted even from a moving vehicle! The young, closed capped specimens are known as Drumsticks.

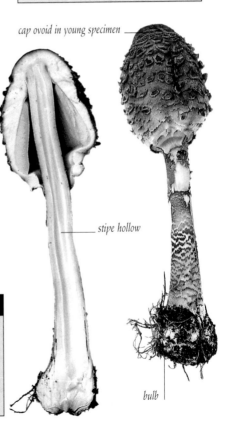

cap ovoid in young specimen

stipe hollow

bulb

EDIBILITY

Very good to eat. Only the cap is edible, the stipe being too coriaceous. When the cap is expanded, the flesh tends to become more elastic. In some places, it is then cooked in batter or breadcrumbs like a cutlet.

MACROLEPIOTA KONRADII

Konrad's Parasol Mushroom

DESCRIPTION: H: 4-5 in (10-13 cm),
Ø: 2³/₄-4¹/₂ in (7-12 cm).
Cap ovoid, then conical, flattened in the
end, with a wide, shallow umbo; the center
is reddish-brown, with a cream margin
covered in small brown spots.
Between them, a series of
large brown scales form
circles radiating from the
center. The gills are
large wide and whitish.
The hollow stipe is rather
bulbous, smooth or finely striped
with reddish-brown, and has a thick,
sliding white ring, edged with gray on
the underside. The flesh is soft and pale,
reddening slightly when cut, especially in
the stipe; no particular odor and flavor.

HABITAT: singly or in groups at the edge
of forests, beside hedgerows, and in clearings. Summer through fall. Fairly common.

gray-brown under the ring

large scales arranged in a star shape

MACROLEPIOTA RHACODES

Shaggy Parasol Mushroom

upturned scales

very large bulb

DESCRIPTION: H: 4¹/₂-8 in (12-20 cm), Ø: 2¹/₂-6 in (6-15 cm). Cap globulose then remaining hemispherical or convex for a long time, has no umbo, fringed margin, reddish and smooth in the center, covered in large brownish, well-spaced brownish scales, making it look hirsute. Gills white or cream, reddening to the touch and when mature. Stipe brittle, hollow and smooth, whitish, reddish-brown to the touch and with age; ring thick and sliding, white and shaggy; very large marginate bulb, often oblique due to curvature of the stipe at the base. Flesh tending to turn carrot or reddish when cut, then turning brownish-red; pleasant odor, mild flavor.

HABITAT: in small groups in well-lit woods and clearings under conifers, especially spruce, Douglas fir, cypress, and beside hedges and in gardens. Summer through fall. Fairly common and widespread.

EDIBILITY

Good to eat. Some minor problems have been reported but they are probably due to confusion with other, very similar varieties of parasol mushroom, such as the *bohemica* variety or the recently aptly-named species *Lepiota venenata*.

POTENTIAL CONFUSION

▶ *LEPIOTA VENENATA*
Venomous Parasol   POISONOUS

MACROLEPIOTA EXCORIATA
Frilly Parasol Mushroom

DESCRIPTION: H: 8-12 cm, Ø: 5-12 cm. Cap domed or conical, umbo small or absent, almost entirely pale brown in the young specimen, subsequently cracking into large scales on a whitish background, except at the center which remains uniformly pale brown; the margin is shaggy. Gills broad and whitish. Stipe smooth and white, no longer than the diameter of the cap, with a base swollen into a small bulb; ring single, white but tinted with pale brown at the edge, conical and ascendent, then sliding along the stipe with age. Flesh white, unchanging; faint odor, mild flavor.

POTENTIAL CONFUSION

▶ *LEPIOTA VENENATA*
Venomous Parasol   POISONOUS

EDIBILITY

Good to eat, though the fibrous stipe should be discarded. Often confused with the Parasol Mushroom.

HABITAT: in groups in well-drained meadows, pastures, and the edge of woods. Late summer through fall. Common in certain regions; widespread.

AMANITA MUSCARIA

Fly Agaric

DESCRIPTION: H: 4-10 in (10-25 cm), Ø: 3¹/₄-8 in (8-20 cm). Cap globulose at first and entirely covered with a white membrane, then flattening completely, bright red dotted with white or yellowish-white pustules which in the younger specimens cover most of the surface. They become more spread out with age and can easily be detached. They tend to disappear with age, and the color turns paler, and may even become pale orange. The gills are crowded, free and broad, white or cream. The stipe is

the white warts are sometimes absent

SPECIAL FEATURES

Hunters of the Cep or Penny Bun Mushroom (*Boletus edulis*) find that the Fly Agaric likes the same habitat as their favorite food. That is why, when hunting for the delicious bolete, they first start looking for places in which the Fly Agaric grows, as it is so easy to spot due to its bright colors.

white, very downy at first, solid then hollow, with a large, fragile, pendant ring which turns slightly yellow and whose thick border may be crenelated; the bulb is topped with two or three floccose or warty ridges. The white flesh is yellow under the cuticle, it has a pleasant odor and mild flavor.

SPECIAL FEATURES

Fly Agaric may take on several different forms. The *aureola* variety is taller and has an orange cap devoid of pustules. It prefers coniferous woods. The *formosa* variety has a cap which varies in color from yellow to bright orange, but the warts on the cap, ring, and stipe are lemon yellow. This particular form is found mostly in North America. All the varieties are poisonous.

The formosa variety has warts (sometimes absent), a ring, and a stipe which are all lemon yellow.

HABITAT: grows in groups or rings, in deciduous or coniferous forests, mainly under birch and spruce; it is often to be found on verges, on acid or siliceous soil. Late summer through fall. Very common everywhere, especially in the mountains and grows in a wide variety of climates.

TOXICITY

The symptoms of poisoning appear three-quarters of an hour after ingestion, through stomach upsets and hallucinations, which may cause hilarity or extreme depression. The Lapps of Siberia have long exploited the hallucinogen properties of the mushroom in their religious rites. It would appear that most of the toxic substances are contained in the cuticle of the cap. This would explain why, in some regions, the mushroom is peeled before eating. In the Middle Ages, it was used as a fly-killer. A few pieces of the cap were soaked in sugared milk to attract the flies which were thus killed, hence the common name of the mushroom.

AMANITA CAESAREA
Caesar's Mushroom

DESCRIPTION: H: 4-7 in (10-18 cm), Ø: 3¼-7 in (8-18 cm). When very young, the whole mushroom is encased in a thick white membrane. The cap is globulose at first, then hemispherical and eventually flattened. It is thick with a clearly striated margin, and a brilliant orange color, slightly viscid in wet weather, smooth but sometimes a few shreds of the universal veil still cling to it. Gills very thick, crowded and broad, pale yellow then deep gold. Stipe thick (¾ to 1¼ in (2 to 3 cm)) becoming bulbous toward the base, striated above the ring, and the same color as the gills. The ring is large and yellow, often striated. The volva is large, thick, and white, flared at the top. Flesh thick and white, yellowing at the periphery; pleasant odor, mild flavor.

HABITAT: deciduous forests, especially oak and chestnut, on acid, well-drained soil. From late summer through early fall. Fairly common in southern Europe, and rarely north of the 45°N latitude, though in warm years it grows as far north as southern Germany and Belgium.

POTENTIAL CONFUSION

▶ *AMANITA MUSCARIA*
Fly Agaric   POISONOUS

EDIBILITY

Excellent, even when raw. Very popular in Italy.

AMANITA PANTHERINA

Panther Cap

DESCRIPTION: H: 3¹⁄₄-6 in (8-15 cm), Ø: 2¹⁄₂-4¹⁄₂ in (6-12 cm).
Cap domed, then convex and finally flat, with a finely striated brown to gray-brown margin, shiny and dotted with little white flakes arranged in more or less concentric circles. Gills crowded, broad and white. Stipe pure white, fibrillose, with a floppy, fugaceous white ring toward the center which has no striations on the upper surface. The bulb is large and can grow to 1¹⁄₂ in (4 cm) in diameter, with a clearly marked upper ridge marginate bulb) topped with a helicoidal floccose ridge winding once or twice around the stipe. Flesh white, thick at the center; slight smell of radish, mild flavor.

HABITAT: grows in small groups on grass verges and deciduous woods, more rarely under conifers. Summer through early fall.

striated margin

Uncommon but fairly widespread.

floccose ridge

POTENTIAL CONFUSION

▶ **AMANITA RUBESCENS**
  The Blusher   EDIBLE
▶ **AMANITA SPISSA**
  False Panther Cap   EDIBLE

SPECIAL FEATURES

A larger variety (var. *abietinum*) grows under mountain conifers, of which the cap, which is darker in color can attain a diameter of 7 in (18 cm).

TOXICITY

Very poisonous, can cause death in certain cases.

AMANITA RUBESCENS

The Blusher

DESCRIPTION: H: 3¼-7 in (8-18 cm), Ø: 3¼-6 in (8-15 cm).

Cap domed then convex, with a margin that is not striated, beige through pale brown, often shaded with dark red, covered in small whitish-pink or pale gray detachable flakes, which are usually very dense in young specimens, more widely spaced and more or less concentric at later stages. Gills broad and crowded, white and spotted with pink, turning pink to the touch. Stipe thick, becoming hollow, thickening toward the base into a bulb with a pointed end; white and striated or smooth above the ring, pinkish white and slightly downy under the ring, clearly marked with crimson on the bulb. Ring wide and pendant, striated and persistent. Flesh white, slowly reddening when cut and when damaged, reddish-brown under the cuticle; odorless but with mild flavor.

SPECIAL FEATURES

The Blusher (*Amanita rubescens*) is a very variable species, of which several varieties are recognized. The *annulosulphurea* variety has a pale sulfur-yellow ring. All varieties retain the same feature of reddening or blushing of the flesh when cut, damaged, or eaten away by insect larvae.

HABITAT: singly or in small groups at the edge of well-lit deciduous or coniferous forests, in highland and lowlands, on acid or slightly calcareous soil. Summer through fall. Very common and widespread.

base of stipe reddening

pale gray or pinkish-gray scales

POTENTIAL CONFUSION

▶ *AMANITA PANTHERINA*
Panther cap   POISONOUS

TOXICITY

Poisonous raw, edible well cooked. The fibrous stem should be discarded.

AMANITA SPISSA

False Panther Cap

DESCRIPTION: H: 3¼-7 in (8-18 cm), Ø: 2¾-4½ in (7-12 cm).
The cap is globulose, then hemispherical and finally flat, sprinkled with pale gray plaques against a brown or olive brown background. The stipe is thick, firm and full, striated above the ring, and marked with grayish zigzag bands below it; the ring full and striated; the bulb is not very marked. Flesh white, thick at the center; it has a faint odor of radish and a mild flavor.

HABITAT: coniferous (especially pine) or deciduous (especially oak), preferably on acid soil. Summer through fall. Widespread but uncommon, more frequently found at altitude.

EDIBILITY

Edible but not worth eating, and should be avoided anyway, due to its close resemblance to the Panther Cap.

SPECIAL FEATURES

This mushroom resembles both the Panther Cap and the Blusher but it does not turn pink or crimson when damaged or cut and there are no clearly marked ridges over the bulb.

POTENTIAL CONFUSION

▶ *AMANITA PANTHERINA*
Panther cap   POISONOUS
▶ *AMANITA RUBESCENS*
The Blusher   EDIBLE

AMANITA JUNQUILLEA, A. GEMMATA
Jonquil Amanita

DESCRIPTION: H: 2¹/₂-4¹/₂ in (6-12 cm), Ø: 2-4 in (5-10 cm).
Cap domed and soon flattening, not very fleshy, with a fleshy, yellow-to-ocher cap and striated margin, often decorated with a few white plaques or flakes. Gills white. Stipe slightly thickened at the base, becoming hollow with age, white and floccose; ring white, median and thin, undeveloped and very fugaceous; the volva disappears fairly quickly, sometimes leaving a ridge above the bulb. Flesh white, pale yellow under the cuticle, odorless and with a mild flavor.

HABITAT: coniferous or deciduous forests, especially pine and beech, on fairly acid soil. Spring through fall. Fairly common in southern parts of the northern hemisphere.

TOXICITY

Some consider it poisonous, others edible. The fact that it has so many variations may mean that it is simply a variety of another species. To be avoided.

AMANITA PHALLOIDES

Death Cap

DESCRIPTION:

H: 3¹/₂-6¹/₂ in (9-17 cm), Ø: 2-6 in (5-15 cm). Cap ovoid or globulose, entirely covered in a white membrane, then hemispherical, and finally flattened; color fairly variable, typically yellowish-green, but also brownish-yellow, olive brown, greenish-brown, and entirely pure white in the *alba* variety, with fine, darker, radial fibrils and sometimes the remains of the white veil. The surface is silky when dry, slightly viscous in wet weather. Gills crowded and broad, white, turning cream with age. Stipe elongated, firm, becoming more or less hollow, slightly thickened toward the base, covered in horizontal, gray-green zigzag bands on a white background. Normally very ample but capable of disappearing and appears to be striated

on the upper surface, white
or slightly greenish;
volva often large,
lobed and white, sur-
rounding a large bulb.
Flesh white, yellow under the cuticle; faint
odor which is unpleasant in older specimens, mild flavor.

ring

TOXICITY

This mushroom is deadly
and has been the cause of
more deaths than all the
other poisonous fungi put
together.

POTENTIAL CONFUSION

▶ **RUSSULA VIRESCENS**
Green Cracking Russula   EDIBLE

▶ **AGARICUS SILVICOLA**
Wood Mushroom   EDIBLE

▶ **TRICHOLOMA PORTENTOSUM**
Pretentious Tricholoma   EDIBLE

volva

There is an entirely white variety of the Death Cap, which looks very similar to the Spring Amanita described below.

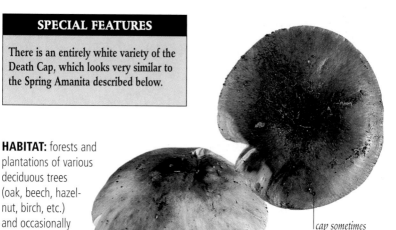

HABITAT: forests and plantations of various deciduous trees (oak, beech, hazelnut, birch, etc.) and occasionally under conifers, from midsummer through fall. Very common, especially in the lowlands. Found all over the world.

cap sometimes brownish in color

yellow-green cap with radiating brown fibrils

The Amanitas are responsible for more than 90% of fatal poisonings caused by wild mushrooms. The seriousness of the poisoning is in direct relationship with the weight of the victim. That is why children are the most vulnerable and when whole families are poisoned they are the first to suffer. About 1¾ oz (50 g) of a deadly species of Amanita is enough to kill an adult, about the weight of A SINGLE MUSHROOM. Symptoms do not appear until between six and 48 hours after ingestion. There is a rapid onset of digestive disorders with nausea, shivering, vomiting, diarrhea, and stomach pain. The symptoms may last several days. A medical examination will reveal more serious damage—the progressive destruction of the liver. Treatment requires hospitalization and may even involve such drastic measures as a liver transplant. Although there has been significant progress in the treatment of poisonings caused by these mushrooms, cases of death are constantly reported by the media in the fall, the height of the picking season, especially in eastern Europe.

AMANITA CITRINA
False Death Cap

DESCRIPTION: H: 2³/₄-5¹/₂ in (7-14 cm), Ø: 2-4 in (5-10 cm).
Cap domed then flattening, lemon yellow with whitish or ocher plaques, entirely white in the *alba* variety. Gills white or pale yellow. Stipe slightly thickening toward the base, pale yellow, with a wide, striated ring, also yellow, and a large bulb (up to 1¹/₄ in (3 cm) in diameter) marginate, whitish, and more or less covered with fragments of the yellow volva. The flesh smells characteristically of raw potato or celeriac.

HABITAT: under deciduous trees or conifers, especially on sandy, acid soil. Late summer through fall. Very common.

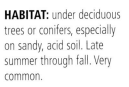

pale lemon yellow cap

bulb globulose

EDIBILITY
Not very good to eat; it was once considered toxic, through confusion with other species.

AMANITA VERNA
Spring Amanita

DESCRIPTION:H: $2^3/_4$-$4^1/_4$ in (7-11 cm), Ø: $1^1/_2$-$4^1/_2$ in (4-12 cm). Cap ovoid or globulose, then hemispherical, eventually flattening, pure white, sometimes cream or beige, smooth, rarely covered in debris of the white veil, matte, viscid when wet. Gills white. Stipe smooth or very slightly floccose, white; ring white, pendant and persistent, but often torn. Volva voluminous and wide, also white. Flesh white; odorless or with a faint, rather unpleasant odor, mild flavor.

HABITAT: copses and airy forests of deciduous trees, especially under oak, rarely under conifers; indifferent to soil type. Mainly found in the spring, but may be encountered in summer, and even early fall. Fairly rare, and mainly found in southern parts of the northern hemisphere. Widespread.

TOXICITY

This mushroom is just as deadly as the Death Cap, but less well known because it is less common, at least in Europe. It is more frequent in the United States.

POTENTIAL CONFUSION

▶ *AGARICUS SILVICOLA*
Wood Mushroom   EDIBLE
▶ *LEUCOAGARICUS LEUCOTHITES*
Off-white Parasol Mushroom EDIBLE

AMANITA VIROSA
Destroying Angel

DESCRIPTION: H: 4-7 in (10-18 cm), Ø: 2-3¼ in (5-8 cm). Cap domed then conical, with a wide umbo, often assymetrical or inclined, pure white and silky, viscid when wet. Gills broad and white with scaly edges. Stipe white, very downy, becoming hollow and stuffed with cottony fibers in older specimens. The ring is very high upon the stipe, sometimes even attached to the gills, but it disappears fairly soon; the bulb at the base is enveloped in a white, sac-like volva. The flesh is white and thick at the center; young specimens have a faint odor which becomes unpleasant in older ones. The flavor is mild.

HABITAT: often under conifers, especially spruce, sometimes under deciduous trees such as beech or birch, on damp, acid soil. From summer through early fall. Fairly common in northern regions and at altitude, rare elsewhere.

TOXICITY

Deadly.

POTENTIAL CONFUSION

▶ *AGARICUS SILVICOLA*
Wood Mushroom   EDIBLE

▶ *LEUCOAGARICUS LEUCOTHITHES*
Off-white Parasol   EDIBLE

AMANITA OVOIDEA
Ovoid Amanita

DESCRIPTION: H: 6-10 in (15-25 cm), Ø: 4¹/₂-10 in (12-25 cm).
Ivory cap very thick and fleshy, remaining ovoid for a long time, smooth, sometimes with a few thick scales and a shaggy margin. Gills whitish, shaggy at the edge. Stipe thick (up to 2 in (5 cm) wide), white and floccose; ring very floccose, becoming detached; ocher volva wide and full, high on the stipe, thick. Flesh white and thick; distinctive odor, mild and pleasant in young specimens, unpleasant in older ones.

HABITAT: under deciduous trees, especially oak, or under conifers, especially pine, in well-lit, grassy woods, on limestone and sandy soil, in warm, sunny locations. Fairly common in the Mediterranean region, rare elsewhere. Summer through fall.

EDIBILITY
Not very good to eat; it must be eaten young, as older specimens produce nausea.

POTENTIAL CONFUSION
▶ *AMANITA PROXIMA* Close Amanita DEADLY

AMANITA VAGINATA

Grisette

DESCRIPTION: H:4-7 in (10-18 cm), Ø: 1½-4 in (4-10 cm).

Cap conical at first then expanding, always fairly umbonate; margin covered in long, deep striations; gray to brun, matte, smooth, and generally without white plaques. Gills crowded, broad and white. Stipe long and slender (up to 8 in (20 cm)), becoming hollow, thickening slightly toward the base where it is about ½ in (1 cm) in diameter; pale gray, bare or slightly floccose, no ring, but with a narrow, white volva around the base, extending 1¼ to 2 in (3 to 5 cm) up the stipe. Flesh very thin under the cap margin; odorless but with a mild   flavor.

HABITAT: Deciduous forests, more rarely under conifers. Summer through fall. Fairly common and widespread.

SPECIAL FEATURES

The Grisette is typical of a group of mushrooms which have several forms or varieties, the main difference being the color of the cap. The commonest of them is the Tawny Grisette d *(Amanita fulva)* which has an orange or fawn cap. The stipe and volva are usually stained with the same color as the cap. It grows mainly under chestnut trees on acid soils. Another feature of the Grisettes is that they have no ring.

TOXICITY

Poisonous raw, good to eat when cooked, but the flesh is thin and fragile.

AMANITA FULVA
Tawny Grisette

The Tawny Grisette has the same characteristics as the Grisette, but it differs in that the cap is orange or fawn, darker in the center , smooth and shiny. The volva and stipe are also spotted with fawn or orange.

HABITAT: deciduous or coniferous woods, especially under chestnut, on acid or siliceous soil. Appears in early summer and lasts through fall. Fairly common.

POTENTIAL CONFUSION
▶ *AMANITA CROCEA*   Saffron Amanita   EDIBLE

EDIBILITY
Good to eat but must be cooked.

AMANITA CROCEA
Saffron Grisette

DESCRIPTION:
H: 4-8 in (10-20 cm),
Ø: 2$\frac{1}{2}$-4$\frac{1}{2}$ in (6-12 cm).
Cap hemispherical at first, then flat, often umbonate, with a clearly striated margin; yellow-orange to reddish orange, paler at the margin. Gills crowded and whitish. Stipe thickening slightly toward the base, brittle, becoming hollow, the same color as the cap and striped with flaky bands. Large volva, white on the outside, pale yellow inside. Flesh white, orange under the cuticle; no particular odor or flavor.

HABITAT: mainly under deciduous trees, often on grass verges on acid soil. Summer through fall. Fairly common in southerly climates, unusual elsewhere.

EDIBILITY
Good to eat.

AMANITA SUBMEMBRANACEA

Gray Grisette

DESCRIPTION: H: 2½-4½ in (6-12 cm), Ø: 1½-2¾ in (4-7 cm).
Cap clearly striated over at least half the area of the radius of the cap, olive brown often with one or two membranous shreds clinging to it, the remains of the veil. Gills white and crowded, flaky at the edge. Stipe thickening slightly toward the base, hollow, white through pale gray, marked with zigzag striations. Volva lobed, fairly frag-ile, pale gray to pale brown. Flesh thick at the center only; odorless, mild flavor.

HABITAT: under conifers, especially spruce. On acid soil. Summer through fall. Fairly common in the mountains, uncommon in low-lying areas.

EDIBILITY

Quite good to eat.

AMANITA BATTARAE, A. UNBRINOLUTEA

Yellow-brown Grisette

DESCRIPTION:
H: 4-6 in (10-15 cm),
Ø: 2½-4½ in (6-12 cm).
Cap conical soon expanding, with a central umbo surrounded by a slight depression, striated over one third of the radius, yellow ocher then turning brownish-yellow, marked with a darker circle in the center. Gills broad, crowded and white. Stipe gradually thickening toward the base, long and hollow with age, spotted with gray on a pale back-ground; white sheath-like volva, deeply embedded in the soil. Flesh white, thick in the center, thin elsewhere, odorless and mild in flavor.

HABITAT: coniferous forests, especially fir and spruce, in the mountains. Rarer under deciduous trees and in mixed woods in the lowlands. Summer through fall. Uncommon.

EDIBILITY

Average eating quality.

THE ENTOLOMATALES

PLUTEUS CERVINUS
Fawn Pluteus

in the center. Gills free, crowded and wide, white at first, then pink. Stipe solid, thickening toward the base, with brown fibrils against a pale background, easily separable from the cap. Flesh thick and white, smelling slightly of radish, mild flavor.

DESCRIPTION: H: 4-6 in (10-15 cm), Ø: 2-6 in (5-15 cm).
Cap conical then flattened, often with a shallow umbo; silky, variable in color, fawn through very dark gray-brown, often darker

HABITAT: singly or in small tufts on the cut side of logs, sawdust, rotting wood, deciduous forests or in parks. From spring through fall. Very frequent and widespread.

PLUTEUS ADMIRABILIS
Admirable Pluteus

DESCRIPTION: H: 1¼-2½ in (3-6 cm), Ø: ½-1¼ in (1-3 cm).
Cap convex then smooth and flat, except in the center where it is wrinkled, orange-yellow to ocher. Gills broad, pale yellow then pinkish. Stipe fragile, smooth and yellow.

HABITAT: singly or in groups on rotting wood. Summer through early fall. In North America only.

EDIBILITY
Good to eat.

SPECIAL FEATURES
The Lion-colored Pluteus (*Pluteus leoninus*) is another yellow species of Pluteus with a smooth cap and white stem.

VOLVARIELLA GLOIOCEPHALA

Pink-spored Grisette

DESCRIPTION: H: 4-7 in (10-18 cm), Ø: 2³/₄-4¹/₂ in (7-12 cm).
Cap ovoid then conical, later convex or expanded, white mouse-gray or gray-brown, smooth, shiny when dry and viscid when damp. Gills crowded, broad and bowed, free from the stipe, pinkish-white then rusty pink or pinkish-brown. Stem thinning toward the top, fibrillose and white, browning at the end, with a very large, very fragile white to gray-brown volva. Flesh whitish, smelling faintly of radish, mild flavor. .

HABITAT: open spaces rich in organic matter, on rotting vegetation. Summer through fall, sometimes as late as December. Fairly common and widespread.

SPECIAL FEATURES

Another species of Volvaria is cultivated throughout southeast Asia on various remains of crops, especially rice.

EDIBILITY

Average edibility.

CLITOPILUS PRUNULUS
Miller

pletely white, velvety or pruinose, rarely pale gray-white. Very decurrent gills, crowded, very supple when pressed with the fingers, easily detachable with a fingernail, white or pale beige, becoming pink upon maturity. Stipe soft and short, often curved and may sometimes be slightly swollen at the base. Flesh thick in the center, very thin at the edge, white, fragile and soft; very pronounced odor and flavor or fresh flour, hence the common name.

HABITAT: in groups in well-lit coniferous or deciduous woods. Late summer through fall, mainly on acid soil. Very common and widespread.

DESCRIPTION: H: 1¹/₂-3¹/₄ in (4-8 cm), Ø: 1¹/₂-4 in (4-10 cm).
Cap convex at first with a tightly inrolled margin, then expanding with a large umbo, or depressed in the center, the margin becoming wavy and torn in places; com-

EDIBILITY

Good to eat, never worm-eaten

POTENTIAL CONFUSION

▶ *CLITOCYBE CANDICANS,*
C. DEALBATA,
C. CERRUSSATA,
White Clitocybes which are POISONOUS

ENTOLOMA CLYPEATUM

Shield-shaped Entoloma

DESCRIPTION: H: 2¹/₂-4¹/₄ in (6-11 cm), Ø: 1¹/₄-4 in (3-10 cm).

Cap conical then convex, margin often undulating and splitting in places, flesh is firm with a very pronounced umbo; the silky, fibrillose surface is beige through gray-brown and very pale when dry, becoming dark gray-brown when wet. Gills broad and well-spaced, white then dirty pink. Stipe fibrillose, whitish or grayish. Flesh white, turning gray when wet. Rancid odor, flavor mild and floury.

HABITAT: in scattered groups under thorn bushes (hawthorn and blackthorn), hedgerows, in parks and on grass verges. Springtime. Common and widespread.

POTENTIAL CONFUSION

▶ *ENTOLOMA LIVIDUM*
Livid Entoloma   POISONOUS

▶ *INOCYBE PATOUILLARDII*
Red-staining Inocybe   POISONOUS

EDIBILITY

Good to eat on condition that it is well cooked.

ENTOLOMA LIVIDUM
Livid Entoloma

DESCRIPTION: H: 4¹/₂-8 in (12-20 cm), Ø: 3¹/₄-6 in (8-15 cm).
Cap hemispherical or conical, becoming convex and eventually flattening, thick and lumpy, with a margin that remains inrolled for a long time, and is then flattened and sinuous. The surface is fibrillose and silky, silvery-gray, ocher-gray, or gray-brown. The gills are very sinuate, pale yellow then salmon pink. Stipe thick, swollen at the base, fibrillose, creamy-white, graying with age. Flesh white, thickening in the center; odor and flavor of fresh flour.

HABITAT: grows in rings or small groups. Sometimes two or three individuals are fused at the base. Found on grass verges and well-lit deciduous woods, especially under oak, beech, and chestnut, on clay and lime-stone soil. Late summer through early fall. Uncommon but widespread.

SPECIAL FEATURES

The Livid Entoloma is responsible for many poisonings due to its resemblance to two edible species, the Clouded Agaric (*Clitocybe nebularis*) and Miller (*Clitopilis prunulus*). It resembles the latter in the strong smell of flour.

TOXICITY

Poisonous. Can cause serious gastro-enteritis.

THE ENTOLOMATALES

ENTOLOMA CETRATUM

Ocelot Entoloma

DESCRIPTION H: 2-3¹/₄ in (5-8 cm),
Ø: ³/₄-1¹/₂ in (2-4 cm).
Cap conical then flattened, with a striated margin, reddish-orange or reddish-brown, becoming ocher when dry, with a darker stain in the center. Gills the same color as the cap, then salmon-pink. Stipe brittle and hollow, expanding at the base, covered in white fibrils on a dark background, lightly powdered white at the top. Flesh brownish-yellow, no particular odor or flavor.

TOXICITY
Probably poisonous.

HABITAT: under conifers, sometimes under deciduous trees, on humid, acid soils, moorland and beside bogs. Summer through fall. Uncommon.

ENTOLOMA CONFERENDUM

Star-spored Entoloma

DESCRIPTION: H: 1¹/₄-3¹/₄ in (3-8 cm),
Ø: ³/₄-1¹/₂ in (2-4 cm).
Cap conical then convex and umbonate, dirty beige when dry, gray-brown and striated on the margin when wet. Gills beige then pinkish. Stipe hollow and brittle, often slightly thickened at the base, strongly striated with silvery fibrils against a beige then brown background. Flesh pale gray, with faint odor and flavor.

HABITAT: pastures and lawns, very wet deciduous or coniferous forests, marshy pinewoods, especially in the mountains. Summer through fall. Common and widespread.

TOXICITY
Poisonous.

ENTOLOMA HIRTIPES
Stinking Entoloma

DESCRIPTION:
H: 3¹/₄-4¹/₂ in (8-12 cm),
Ø: 1¹/₄-2³/₄ in (3-7 cm).
Cap conical, then flattening with small pointed umbo, silky and reddish-brown or dark brown when damp, becoming paler when dry, with a striated margin. Gills broad, white to pale brown. Stipe long and slender (4 in x ¹/₄ in

(10 cm x 0.6 cm)) expanding at the bulbous, gray-brown base sprinkled with white powder at the top. Rancid odor of fish oil. Flesh gray or pale brown, mild and floury flavor.

HABITAT: in coniferous or mixed woods on limestone soil. Spring. Fairly common.

ENTOLOMA RHODOPOLIUM
Silky-stem Entoloma

DESCRIPTION: H: 3¹/₄-6 in (8-15 cm),
Ø: 1¹/₂-4 in (4-10 cm).
Cap convex then expanding, depressed or umbilicate in the center, beige in dry weather, turning gray-brown when wet, with a margin that becomes undulating with age, and which is sometimes striated. Gills creamy-white then dark pink. Stipe fragile, thickening slightly toward the base and at the top, smooth, silky, and whitish. Flesh thin and white; no particular odor or flavor.

HABITAT: in groups in deciduous woods, especially beech, sometimes under conifers. Late summer through fall. Frequent, but commoner on higher ground. Widespread.

TOXICITY
Poisonous.

ENTOLOMA SERICEUM
Silky Entoloma

DESCRIPTION: H: 1½-4 in (4-10 cm), Ø: ¾-2 in (2-5 cm).
Cap conical then convex with a small umbo, margin with long striations when wet, silky gray when dry, dark brown almost black when wet. Gills sinuate, dirty white then dirty pink. Stipe thin, hollow, and friable, grayish with white fibrils Flesh gray; strong odor and flavor of flour.

TOXICITY
Poisonous.

HABITAT: lawns and well-drained grassland, from lowland to highland. Late summer through fall. Common.

ENTOLOMA SERRULATUM
Blue Entoloma

DESCRIPTION: H: 1½-2¾ in (4-7 cm), Ø: ½-1½ in (1-4 cm).
Cap conical then convex but very often umbilicate or depressed in the center, felted or fibrillose, dark blue-gray or blue-black. Gills very broad, pale blue then violet-brown, with saw-toothed edges. Stipe solid then hollow, smooth and silky, the same color as the cap, felted with white mycelium at the base.

HABITAT: in meadows, on lawns, at roadsides and on verges, in highland and lowland. Late summer through fall. Uncommon.

TOXICITY
Poisonous.

THE CORTINARIALES

CORTINARIUS ORELLANUS

Annatto Cortinarius

DESCRIPTION: H: 2¹/₂-4¹/₂ in (6-12 cm),
Ø: 1¹/₄-3¹/₄ in (3-8 cm).
Cap bell-shaped, then convex, finally expanded, with or without a central umbo. The margin becomes sinuate and split. Surface fibrillose or finely granulose, bright reddish-orange or reddish-brown. Gills widely spaced on broad, yellow-orange then bright red. Stipe sometimes slightly bent and narrowing at the base, the same color as the cap or paler, sometimes displaying yellow filaments of the cortina. Flesh golden; odor of radish or potato, slightly acid flavor.

HABITAT: deciduous forests, especially oak, sometimes under conifers (pines), on dry, acid soil, in mountains and plains. From late summer through fall. Generally uncommon but may be abundant in some years.

reddish-brown cap

SPECIAL FEATURES

This mushroom was once called the Mountain Cortinarius, because it was thought that the name of the species (*orellanus*) came from "oros" meaning "mountain" in Greek. In fact, it is found in the plains as well as in the mountains. The name is an allusion to a tropical shrub tropical named Annatto (*Bixia orellana*) whose seeds are exactly the same color as this Cortinarius.

TOXICITY

Deadly. The symptoms of poisoning do not manifest themselves until three days after ingestion, and in certain cases the first symptoms do not appear until two weeks later.

THE CORTINARIALES

CORTINARIUS SPECIOSISSIMUS, C. RUBELLUS
Suspect Cortinarius

DESCRIPTION: H: 2¹/₂-4¹/₂ in (6-12 cm),
Ø: 1¹/₂-3¹/₄ in (4-8 cm).
Conical or bell-shaped cap expanding later, with
a pointed umbo, downy, orange brown, fawn,
or reddish. Gills widely spaced, the same color
as the cap. Stipe fairly long, thickening at the
base but thinning in the ground; reddish with a
few faint yellow circular marks. Flesh yellow or
red, faint odor of radish and mild flavor.

TOXICITY
Deadly.

HABITAT: mainly forests of spruce, on
humid and acid soil. Late summer through
mid-fall. Uncommon.

CORTINARIUS TRAGANUS
Stinking Cortinarius

DESCRIPTION: H: 3¹/₄-4¹/₂ in (8-12 cm),
Ø: 2-4¹/₂ in (5-12 cm).
Cap hemispherical then expanded, fleshy, with
silky bluish-lilac veil then dirty white, more or
less mixed with blue. Widely spaced, sinuate,
bright saffron gills, turning rust-colored. Sturdy
stipe, thickening toward the base, bulbous and
slightly paler than the cap. Flesh the same color as the
gills. darker darker in the stipe. The odor is unusual but hard
to define, though rather unpleasant, but sometimes
fruity; bitter flavor.

SPECIAL FEATURES
The Camphor Cortinarius *(Cortinarius camphoratus)* is very similar. Its stronger odor is extremely unpleasant, and the flesh is tinted blue or violet. The gills are violet prior to maturity.

HABITAT: deciduous
or coniferous forests,
usually in the mountains,
on acid soil. Summer through
mid-fall. Common.

CORTINARIUS ANOMALUS

Abnormal Cortinarius

DESCRIPTION: H: 3¼-4½ in (8-12 cm), Ø: 1¼-3¼ in (3-8 cm).

Cap convex then expanded, with or without a large umbo, with a regular then undulating margin, grayish-ocher, yellow-brown, or reddish, sometimes violet on the margin, and sprinkled with brilliant specks like mica. Gills violet, soon turning rust-brown. Stipe often twice as long as the diameter of the cap, bending, thickening toward the base, blue-violet toward the top, white or reddish-white toward the bottom. There are reddish rings on the stipe which disappear with age. The flesh is whitish-violet in the cap, violet at the top of the stipe; faint odor, mild flavor.

HABITAT: in groups in deciduous forests (birch) or beneath conifers (pine), in the lowlands and highlands. Late summer through fall. Very common.

CORTINARIUS ALBOVIOLACEUS

Mauve-tinted Cortinarius

DESCRIPTION: H: 2³⁄₄-5¹⁄₂ in (7-14 cm), Ø: 1¹⁄₂-3¹⁄₄ in (4-8 cm). Cap campanulate then flattening, often with a very large umbo, pale lilac or pale violet, covered in a silky white veil at first, then covered in silky fibrils, but never viscid. Gills violet-gray then turning reddish-brown. Stipe fairly thick, very swollen at the base, often slight bowed, the same color as the cap, with a white cortina becoming rust-spotted toward the top. Flesh thick in the center of the cap, thin at the edge, pale violet or bluish, especially at the top of the stipe; odorless, mild flavor.

HABITAT: often in groups in deciduous forests (oak, beech, chestnut), sometimes under conifers. Prefers acid soils. Summer through fall. Very common.

CORTINARIUS SEMISANGUINEUS

Semi-sanguine Cortinarius

DESCRIPTION: H: 2-4 in (5-10 cm), Ø: 1¼-2¾ in (3-7 cm).
Cap campanulate then flattening with a small umbo, surface shiny and covered in cinnamon or yellow-brown fibrillose granulations, sometimes darker in the center. Stipe long and flexible, pale yellow, with a few reddish fibrils, sometimes pinkish-orange at the base; thin, yellowish cortina. Flesh golden yellow or ocher olive; odor and flavor of radish.

HABITAT: coniferous or mixed lowland and mountain forests. In the fall. Common.

TOXICITY
Poisonous.

CORTINARIUS CINNAMOMEUS

Cinnamon Cortinarius

DESCRIPTION: H: 2-4 in (5-10 cm), Ø: 1¾-2¼ in (3-6 cm.
Cap convex then flattened, often umbonate, cinnamon-colored, olive or reddish-brown. Gills yellow-orange, turning rust when mature. Stipe flexible, thickening toward the bottom, hollow, yellow to reddish, scaly toward the bottom. Flesh lemon yellow; faint odor and bitter flavor.

HABITAT: in groups in coniferous forests (mainly spruce and pine), rarer under deciduous trees, on acid and very humid, even boggy ground. Late summer through fall. Fairly common and widespread.

TOXICITY
Very poisonous.

CORTINARIUS ARMILLATUS
Red-banded Cortinarius

DESCRIPTION: H: 4-6¾ in (10-17 cm), Ø: (5-12 cm).

Cap flattened bell-shape, fleshy, reddish and covered with very small, slightly darker scales, often bearing the remains of the red veil on the margin. Beige gills soon becoming rust-colored. Stipe firm, full, with a large bulb, ringed with brick-red. sometime oblique circles. Cortina white, abundant but ephemeral. Flesh pale brown, odor of radish, mild or bitter flavor.

TOXICITY
Suspected of being poisonous.

HABITAT: in groups under deciduous trees, mainly birch on heathland and very acid and humid soil, in highlands or lowlands. Late summer through fall. Fairly common.

CORTINARIUS TORVUS
Curved Cortinarius

DESCRIPTION: H: 3¼-5½ in (8-14 cm), Ø: 2-4 in (5-10 cm). Cap hemispherical then convex, fleshy, with fine brown or grayish-brown fibrils, sometimes slightly violet. Gills thick and very widely spaced, gray-violet then rust. Stipe thickening at the base, often curved, violet toward the top, covered underneath with a whitish sheath the top of which is incurved to form a sort of ring. Flesh gray and thick in the center, violet at the top of the stipe; strong and unpleasant odor and mild flavor.

HABITAT: deciduous forests, mainly beech. Summer through fall. Very common.

whitish sheath forming a ring near the top of the stipe

CORTINARIUS HINNULEUS
Fawn Cortinarius

DESCRIPTION: H: 2¾-4¾ in (7-12 cm), Ø: 2-3¼ in (5-8 cm).

Cap bell-shaped then expanding, with a prominent umbo and margin incurved for a long time, yellow ocher to reddish-brown, fibrillose. Gills widely-spaced and wide, violet at first then the same color as the cap. Stipe ocher, covered in rings of whitish veil forming a white ring around the middle of the stipe. Flesh whitish, tinged with violet at the top of the stipe; odor of earth or mold, mild flavor turning bitter after a few moments of chewing.

HABITAT: in all types of forest and on all types of soil, in plains and mountains. Summer through fall. Common.

CORTINARIUS PALEACEUS
Straw Cortinarius

DESCRIPTION: H: (4-8 cm), Ø: (2-3 cm). Cap campanulate or conical, then flattening, with a large brownish-gray pointed umbo, becoming much paler when dry, covered with fine pointed white scales which become scarcer with age. Gills cream then turning brown. Stipe long and sinuous, brownish-gray striped with white, sometimes with a white ring which is more or less apparent. Flesh thin, dark brown when wet, ocher in dry conditions, with a strong odor of geranium.

HABITAT: on moss in coniferous or mixed forests of birch and conifers, on very wet ground. Fall. Uncommon to fairly common.

TOXICITY
Suspected of being poisonous.

CORTINARIUS FLEXIPES
Flexible-stem Cortinarius

DESCRIPTION: H: 1¾-3¼ in (4-8 cm), Ø: ¾-1¾ (2-4 cm). Cap conical then flattened, with a pointed umbo and slightly fibrillose surface, blackish-brown when wet, paler in dry weather. The paler margin is covered with the remains of the white veil. Gills grayish to rust brown with lilac highlights. Stipe thin, pale gray-brown, sometimes tinged with pale lilac at the top, and carrying white flakes arranged in rings except at top. Flesh brown or violet-brown, lilac at the top of the stipe; odorless and flavorless.

HABITAT: in small tufts or singly, under spruce, often in moss, alongside birches or in very humid soil. Late summer and fall. Fairly frequent in places.

CORTINARIUS MULTIFORMIS

Multiform Cortinarius

DESCRIPTION: H:2¼-4 in (6-10 cm), Ø:2-4 in (5-10 cm).

Cap fleshy, convex for a long time, then flattened, with a margin that remains inrolled for a long time. Viscid at first, fawn ocher, reddish-ocher, later darkening to *café-au-lait,* striated with darker fibrils and with an opaque veil which masks the color of the cap. Gills whitish or beige, then rust-brown. Stipe white or beige, yellowing, ending in a more or less marginate bulb, ¾ to 1¼ in (2 to 3 cm) in diameter. Flesh white, yellowing, faint in young specimens, becoming more or less fruity or smelling of honey with age and mild in flavor.

SPECIAL FEATURES

This is a collective species, consisting of several forms and varieties.

HABITAT: under deciduous or coniferous trees in lowland or mountains. Summer and fall. Common.

CORTINARIUS CAERULESCENS

Blue Cortinarius

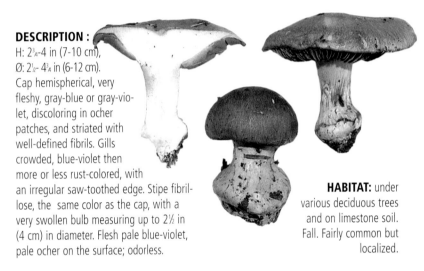

DESCRIPTION :
H: 2¾-4 in (7-10 cm),
Ø: 2½- 4¾ in (6-12 cm).
Cap hemispherical, very fleshy, gray-blue or gray-violet, discoloring in ocher patches, and striated with well-defined fibrils. Gills crowded, blue-violet then more or less rust-colored, with an irregular saw-toothed edge. Stipe fibrillose, the same color as the cap, with a very swollen bulb measuring up to 2½ in (4 cm) in diameter. Flesh pale blue-violet, pale ocher on the surface; odorless.

HABITAT: under various deciduous trees and on limestone soil. Fall. Fairly common but localized.

CORTINARIUS PURPURASCENS

Purplish Cortinarius

DESCRIPTION: H: 2½-4¾ in (6-12 cm),
Ø: 2-6 in (5-15 cm).
Cap hemispherical then expanded and lumpy with undulating margin, fleshy, viscid, reddish-brown with margin that is sometimes violet and fibrillose. Gills violet then rust becoming violet when rubbed. Stipe violet, very fibrillose, even striated, turning deeper violet; bulb fairly large. Violet flesh, the color intensifying when exposed to the air. Faint odor, mild flavor.

HABITAT:
under conifers and sometimes under deciduous trees on limestone soil. Fall. Fairly common.

violet and purple coloration over the whole mushroom

CORTINARIUS CALOCHROUS
Many-colored Cortinarius

Cap convex soon flattening, pale lemon to yellow ocher, dotted with red in the center. Gills crowded, pale violet-pink then brownish-violet or rust-colored, with saw-toothed edges. Stipe ½ in (1 cm) in diameter, up to 1¼ to 2¼ in (3 à 4 cm) at the bulb. White then yellow or ocher; bulb whitish and marginate; cortina ocher and abundant. Flesh white, lilac at the top of the stipe, almost odorless and with a mild flavor.

DESCRIPTION: H: 1½-2¾ in (4-7 cm), Ø: 2-2¾ in (5-7 cm).

HABITAT: under beeches, but sometimes in mixed woods on limestone soil. Fall. Fairly common.

CORTINARIUS GLAUCOPUS
Green-stemmed Cortinarius

DESCRIPTION: H: 2-4¾ in (5-12 cm), Ø: 2-4 in (5-10 cm).

Cap convex, very firm, with an inrolled margin, yellow orange or fawn, with reddish, well-defined fibrils. Gills pale lilac at first then rust-colored. Stipe short and thick, bluish or lilac at the top, yellowish-white toward the base, with a narrow, conical, marginate bulb. Flesh firm and whitish, bluish at the top of the stipe; faint odor and mild flavor.

HABITAT: in groups or circles in coniferous forests at all altitudes on limestone soil; summer through early fall. Common.

CORTINARIUS ELEGANTISSIMUS

Elegant Cortinarius

DESCRIPTION: H: 2¾-4¾ in (7-12 cm),
Ø: 2½-4 in (6-10 cm).
Cap convex then expanding, though the margin remains inrolled, viscid in wet weather, brilliant sulfur yellow, reddening from the center. Gills bright yellow, then olive. Stipe ending in a very large yellow bulb, which later turns brown. Flesh pale violet at the top of the stipe, sulfur yellow in the bulb, white to pale yellow elsewhere; pleasant odor, mild flavor.

HABITAT: beech forests on limestone soil. Fall. Fairly common.

EDIBILITY

Edible, but there is a serious risk of potential confusion with the Resplendent Cortinarius which is deadly.

POTENTIAL CONFUSION

▶ *CORTINARIUS SPLENDENS*
Resplendent Cortinarius   DEADLY

CORTINARIUS SPLENDENS

Resplendent Cortinarius

DESCRIPTION: H: 2-4 in (5-10 cm),
Ø: 1½-2¾ in (4-7 cm).
Cap like that of the Elegant Cortinarius but more golden. Gills bright yellow then rust-colored upon maturity. Stipe has a large marginate, sulfur yellow bulb, tinged with rust toward the bottom, cortina lemon yellow. The flesh is bright yellow all over and uniform. Odorless, mild flavor.

HABITAT: in small groups in deciduous forests, on limestone soil. Fall. Uncommon.

TOXICITY

Deadly, the poison attacks the kidneys.

CORTINARIUS RUFOOLIVACEUS
Reddish-olive Cortinarius

DESCRIPTION:
H: 2½-4¾ in (6-12 cm),
Ø: 2¾-4¾ in (7-12 cm).
Cap hemispherical
then convex, viscid,
brownish-red or russet, slightly
violet or olive at the edge.
Gills very crowded, olivaceous
then cinnamon. Stipe yellow-
green, violet at the top, but often
entirely violet due to the abundant cortina; bulb marginate and reddening. Flesh firm and thick, rusty pink in the bulb, purplish-violet; faint odor and bitter taste.

HABITAT: in small groups in deciduous forests, especially oak and beech, on limestone soil. Fall. Fairly common.

CORTINARIUS DELIBUTUS
Glutinous Cortinarius

DESCRIPTION: H: 2¾-4¾ in (7-12 cm), Ø: 3-8 cm.
Cap convex then expanded, very viscid, lemon to golden. Gills violet then orange to cinnamon. Stipe elongated, thickening into a bulb at the base, whitish, sometimes bluish at the top, edged with filaments tinted orange yellow. Lilac flesh in young speci-mens, turning whitish but often the top of the stipe retains its violet color; faint odor, not particularly characteristic, mild or bitter flavor.

HABITAT: in groups in deciduous forests often with birch and beech and in mixed forests in the plains and mountains. Late summer through fall. Common.

CORTINARIUS TRIVIALIS
Trivial Cortinarius

DESCRIPTION: H: 3¼-7¾ in (8-14 cm),
Ø: 1½-4 in (4-10 cm).
Cap conical and convex then flattened and more or less lumpy, very viscid, yellow ocher, fawn or brownish-yellow. Gills grayish- ocher or grayish-violet, soon turning rusty, hidden at first by a viscid cortina. Stipe very rigid and very long, up to 6 in (15 cm), thinner at the base, very viscid, ringed with circular ridges. Flesh pale yellow, ocher brown in the lower part of the stipe; odorless, mild flavor.

HABITAT: in large groups in deciduous woods (oak, beech, birch). Late summer through fall. Common.

HEBELOMA CRUSTULINIFORME
Poison Pie

straw-colored, ocher or red, darker in the center, slightly viscid when wet. Gills the same color, weeping tiny drops in young specimens which dry leaving a brown mark. Stipe ¼-½ in (1 to 2 cm) in diameter, slightly bulbous and floccose at the top. Flesh thick and white; more or less strong odor of radish, bitter taste.

HABITAT: in groups in damp places in deciduous or coniferous forests. Summer through fall. Very common.

DESCRIPTION: H: 2-4 in (5-10 cm),
Ø: 2-4 in (5-10 cm).
Cap convex then flattening, margin remaining inrolled for a long time, often umbonate,

TOXICITY
Poisonous, causes serious gastro-enteritis.

HEBELOMA MESOPHAEUM

Brown-centered Hebeloma

DESCRIPTION: H: 2-4 in (5-10 cm),
Ø: 1¼-2¾ in (3-7 cm).
Cap convex then flattened often umbonate, slightly viscid in wet weather, typically two-colored. The center is reddish-brown and the outer part paler due to the presence of the remains of the whitish veil (cortina). Gills pale, subsequently turning brown. Stipe whitish, later reddish-brown at the base, with a fibrillose annular zone at the base. Flesh white, ocher to brown at the base of the stipe; strong odor of radish, bitter flavor.

HABITAT: in groups on lawns, in parks, in grassy clearings in deciduous or coniferous forests, mainly in the mountains. Late summer through fall. Fairly common.

HEBELOMA SINAPIZANS

Mustard Hebeloma

DESCRIPTION:
H: 4-8 in (10-20 cm),
Ø: 2¾-6 in (7-15 cm).
Cap convex then expanded, reddish-ocher roux to pale brown, paler at the margin. Gills beige or ocher, then rust brown. Stipe whitish and long, up to 8 in (20 cm), swollen at the base and becoming hollow. Flesh whitish; a cone of fibers descends from the center of the cap into the top of the hollow stipe; odor of radish, very peppery taste.

SPECIAL FEATURES

Looks like Poison Pie (*Hebeloma crustiliniforme*) but larger. The cone of fibers visible at the top of the stipe in vertical section, is very distinctive in this species.

HABITAT: in large groups under beech, oak, or hornbeam, or in parks. Summer and fall. Common.

TOXICITY

Poisonous.

HEBELOMA RADICOSUM
Rooting Hebeloma

DESCRIPTION: H: 2¾-8 in (7-20 cm), Ø: 2-4¾ in (5-12 cm). Cap convex, fleshy, viscous, reddish ocher , slightly scaly. Gills crowded, pale at first then browning rapidly. Stipe ½ to 1 in (1 to 2.5 cm) thick, with a scaly, white ring and powdery at the top, the same color as the cap and covered with scales below the ring, swollen at the base but with a thick pseudorrhiza which roots into the soil. Flesh white with a very strong odor of bitter almonds, mild flavor.

HABITAT: deciduous forests, mainly beech. Summer through fall. Fairly common.

rooting base

ALNICOLA MELINOIDES, NAUCORIA ESCHAROIDES
Yellowish Naucoria

DESCRIPTION: H: 2-3¼ in (5-8 cm), Ø: ½-1¼ in (1-3 cm). Cap convex then flat, sometimes umbonate, the margin becoming striated then undulating, yellowish-red or dirty ocher when dry, reddish-brown when wet, darker in the center. Gills crowded, ocher at first then taking on a dark brown coloration. Stipe long and slender (about 2¾-x ¹⁄₁₆ in (7 x 0.3 cm)), the same color as cap, but darkening from the base with age, and covered with very fine down at the top. The small bulb is paler at the base. Flesh odorless, slightly bitter.

HABITAT: in large groups on moss in damp shady areas with alder or willow on river banks. Summer through fall. Common.

INOCYBE DULCAMARA
Bittersweet Inocybe

DESCRIPTION:
H: 1¼-2 in (3-5 cm),
Ø: ¾-2 in (2-5 cm).
Cap convex, eventually flattened, not fleshy fibrillose and scaly, yellow ocher or fawn, at first covered with a white cortina. Gills ocher then brown. Stipe cylindrical and short, the same color as the cap, and like it, occasionally bearing the remains of a cortina when young, and sometimes a faint cottony ring. Flesh pale brown; faint odor and more or less bitter flavor.

HABITAT: in thinly wooded areas, bare ground, fallow land, and lawns. Summer through fall. Common.

INOCYBE RIMOSA, I. FASTIGIATA
Hoar-frost Inocybe

DESCRIPTION: H: 1¼-2¾ in (3-7 cm),
Ø: 1¼-2¼ in (3-8 cm).
Cap conical, then more expanded with a large pointed umbo; the surface is very fibrillose, cracked, straw colored, pale yellow or ocher, and the margin cracks deeply with age. Gills crowded, yellow-green or yellow-gray, then turning brown, with white edges. Stipe paler, stained with ocher at the base, pruinose or slightly scaly at the top. White flesh, with a faint but unpleasant odor, mild, slightly bitter flavor.

HABITAT: deciduous forests, sometimes of conifers, especially on grass verges or forest clearings, on well-drained sandy or limestone soil. Summer through fall. Common.

TOXICITY
Poisonous.

INOCYBE PATOUILLARDII
Red-Staining Inocybe

SPECIAL FEATURES

This mushroom can be identified by the way every part of it turns red either to the touch or naturally with age. It is very poisonous and has caused deaths.

DESCRIPTION: H: 2-3½ in (5-9 cm), Ø: 1¼-2¼ in(3-8 cm).
Cap conical, umbonate and fibrillose, splitting at the margin, whitish to straw-colored, reddening to the touch and with age. Gills pale, then brown, reddening when damaged or rubbed. Stipe sturdy, ½ to ¾ in (1 to 2.5 cm) in diameter, white and red. Flesh white, reddening in the stipe when cut, and mild flavor.

HABITAT: in well-lit woods, footpaths, clearings, and parks. Late spring through early fall. Uncommon to fairly common depending on the year and the location.

tendency to redden in places.

POTENTIAL CONFUSION

▶ *CALOCYBE GAMBOSA*
  St George's Mushroom   EDIBLE
▶ *ENTOLOMA CLYPEATUM,
  E. APRILE, E. SEPIUM*
  Spring Entolomas   EDIBLE

TOXICITY

Deadly.

INOCYBE MACULATA
Spotted Inocybe

right to the center. Spotted with white in young specimens. Gills turning olive-gray . Stipe thickening at the base, sometimes bulbous and fibrillose, white but reddish in the center, browning with age and from the top. Flesh has a specific odor that is hard to define.

HABITAT: under deciduous trees (hornbeam, beech) on damp, limestone soil, on paths and in ash groves. fall. Fairly common.

DESCRIPTION: H: 1¾-3¼ in (4-8 cm),
Ø: 1¼-2¼ in (3-8 cm)
Cap conical then flatter, with pointed umbo, and reddish-brown fibrils on a cream background, deeply cracked in places, sometimes

TOXICITY
Poisonous.

INOCYBE CALAMISTRATA
Crimped Inocybe

DESCRIPTION: H: 2-3¼ in (5-8 cm),
Ø: 2-3¼ in (5-8 cm).
Cap campanulate or convex, dark brown, covered in upturned dark scales, gills broad, whitish but soon turning reddish-brown, stipe often twisted, dark brown like the cap, covered in erect scales, often with dark-blue base. Flesh white but pink when cut, bluegreen in the base of the stipe; odor unpleasant, mild flavor.

HABITAT: under deciduous or coniferous trees, often birch or spruce on very damp soil. Summer and fall. Uncommon.

TOXICITY
Poisonous.

INOCYBE CORYDALINA
Green-capped Inocybe

DESCRIPTION: H: 3¼-5¼ in (8-13 cm), Ø: 1¾-2¾ in (4-7 cm).
Bell-shaped then flattened, umbonate, fibrillose cap, cream at first then turning brown, with a pale green umbo. Gills white, turning gray. Stipe long, the base swollen into a bulb, white at first, then striated with brown fibrils. very strong, unusual fruity odor, mild flavor.

HABITAT: singly in deciduous forests on limestone or non-acid soil. Late summer through fall. Fairly common.

TOXICITY
Very poisonous.

SPECIAL FEATURES
The odor is similar to that of Corydalis a spring flower from which it has received its botanical epithet.

INOCYBE PUSIO
Dwarf Inocybe

DESCRIPTION:
H: 1¾-2 in (2-5 cm), Ø: ½-1¼ in (1-3 cm).
Cap very fibrillose or streaky with a wide umbo, brownish, with a lilac margin. Gills pale gray then gray-brown. Stipe pruinose at the extremity, especially in young specimens, with a small bulb at the base, ocher or violet at the top in young speci-mens, with a few reddish fibrillose filaments. Flesh lilac-colored at the top of the stipe; odor unpleasant.

HABITAT: under deciduous trees or spruce on very humid soil. Summer through fall. Common.

TOXICITY
Suspected of being poisonous.

INOCYBE LACERA
Torn-cap Inocybe

DESCRIPTION: H: 1½ -2¼ in (4-6 cm),
Ø: ¾-1½ in (2-4 cm).
Cap conical, fibrillose and downy, with an inrolled, split margin, reddish-brown or grayish-brown, sometimes grayish-yellow. Gills rust-colored, with white edges. Stipe about ⅛ in (4 mm) wide, slightly bulbous, devoid of down, with a cortina in the young specimen, ocher, blackening at the base. Flesh pale in the cap, darker in the stipe; mild flavor, unpleasant odor.

HABITAT: moorland, on bare soil beside paths, on sandy, poor soil. Fall. Fairly common.

SPECIAL FEATURES
One of the rare species of Inocybes to be completely free of down on the stipe.

TOXICITY
Suspected of being poisonous.

INOCYBE GODEYI
Godey's Inocybe

DESCRIPTION: H: 1¾-2¾ in (4-7 cm),
Ø: ¾-1½ in (2-4 cm).
Cap conical then flattening with a central umbo, fibrillose or streaky, often split along the margin, cream or beige, becoming reddish-orange. Gills the same shade as the cap. Stipe with marginate bulb, white then striated with red. Bulb remaining white. Flesh white, reddening in contact with the air; strong and unpleasant odor, acrid taste.

HABITAT: deciduous forests, mainly beech, on limestone soil. Fall. Fairly common in the south.

TOXICITY
Suspected of being poisonous.

INOCYBE GEOPHYLLA
Common White Inocybe

Common White Inocybe, lilacina variety.

DESCRIPTION: H: 1¼-2¼ in (3-6 cm), Ø: ½-2½ in (1-4 cm). Cap conical and pointed then flattening with a prominent umbo and smooth, white, silky surface, sometimes viscid at first and ocher on the umbo. Gills crowded and swollen, cream or pale gray, then brownish-ocher. Stipe long and slender, swollen into a small bulb at the base. At first covered with a large cortina, then fibrillose and with a downy top. Flesh white or cream, unpleasant odor and mild flavor or slightly acrid flavor.

SPECIAL FEATURES

This species contains many varieties, the commonest of which is the *lilacina* variety, which is purple except for the umbo, which remains ocher.

HABITAT: deciduous forests, especially on clay and limestone soil. Summer through fall. very common.

TOXICITY

Very poisonous.

INOCYBE ASTEROSPORA
Star-spored Inocybe

DESCRIPTION: H: 2¼-4 in (6-10 cm), Ø: 1¼-2¼ in (3-6 cm).
Cap conical then flattened and umbonate, split up to the umbo, reddish or reddish-brown, but with white flesh showing through the cracks. Gills dirty beige then cinnamon. Stipe slender, entirely pruinose and striated, reddish, orange or brownish-red, ending abruptly at the base in a flattened white, turnip-shaped bulb. Flesh pale reddish, darker in the stipe; no particular odor.

HABITAT: under deciduous trees. It appears to show a preference for hazelnut and beech. Fall. Very common.

TOXICITY
Poisonous.

bulb white and flattened

ROZITES CAPERATA
Wrinkled Rozites

DESCRIPTION: H: 3¼-6 in (8-15 cm), Ø: 2¼-4¾ in (6-12 cm).
Cap globulose then campanulate, very fleshy in the center, with a wrinkled or lumpy surface, except in the center, yellow-orange or ocher; the surface is covered with a white or bluish-white down in young specimens and this persists in the center of the cap in mature specimens. Gills pale then ocher, with ragged edges. Stipe bulbous or thickened at the base, fibrous, slightly downy above the striated and persistent ring. Flesh whitish; pleasant odor and mild flavor.

EDIBILITY
Good to eat but often worm-eaten. The fibrous stipe should be discarded.

HABITAT: in groups in coniferous woods (pine, spruce) or deciduous woods (oak, beech) on acid or sandy soil. Late summer through fall. Fairly common in mid-mountain.

GYMNOPILUS PENETRANS

Penetrating Gymnopilus

DESCRIPTION: H: 2¼-4 in (7-10 cm), Ø: 1¼-2¾ in (3-7 cm).
Cap convex then expanded, fibrillose, yellow-orange to rust, paler at the edge. Gills yellow then brownish-orange. Stipe thickening from top to bottom, whitish to yellow with darker fibrils, and base covered in white down; small, fragile, faint ring. Flesh whitish, odorless and very bitter.

HABITAT: singly or in tufts on rotting branches or twigs of conifers, sometimes partially buried in the ground; also on the cones. Summer through fall. Very common.

TOXICITY
Poisonous.

GYMNOPILUS SPECTABILIS
Fiery Agaric

DESCRIPTION: H: 4-7¼ in (10-18 cm), Ø: 2-6 in (5-15 cm).
Cap convex, orange-yellow to fawn, with reddish fibrils. Gills sinuate, bright yellow, then rust-colored, browning to the touch. Stipe thick, wider at the base, with a well-developed ring, rust to yellow; flesh thick and firm, whitish to pale yellow, faint odor and bitter flavor.

HABITAT: in small tufts or singly, at the base of stumps, on branches and dead trunks of deciduous trees, rarer on conifers. Summer through fall. Uncommon.

TOXICITY
Poisonous and hallucinogenic. Suspected of being responsible for some serious cases of poisoning.

CREPIDOTUS MOLLIS
Soft Crepidotus

DESCRIPTION: Ø: ¾-2¾ in (2-7 cm).
Cap bell-shaped or expanded into shell-shape or kidney-shape, whitish to beige when dry, ocher to brownish-gray when damp. Surface covered with a very viscid detachable film. Gills crowded, whitish then brown, radiating from the point of attachment. Stipe absent or very short and lateral. Flesh gelatinous.

HABITAT: in imbricated or tiered groups on dead wood, stumps or fallen branches of various deciduous trees. Present all year round. Very common.

CREPIDOTUS VARIABILIS

Variable Crepidotus

DESCRIPTION: Ø: ¼-1¼ in (0.5-3 cm).
Cap pure white and kidney-shaped, felted;
upper surface often attached to the support, so
that the fungus has its gills uppermost. The
gills radiate from the point of attachment and
change from cream to pinkish-red, and finally
to cinnamon. The stipe is absent. The flesh is
thin, white, and odorless. This species is inedible mainly due to its small size.

HABITAT: in tiered groups or aligned along
branches and twigs of deciduous trees, especially in brushwood or in massed branches.

Very common in the fall, though it occasionally persists throughout the year.

GALERINA LAEVIS

Smooth Galerina

DESCRIPTION: H: ¾-1¾ in (2-4 cm),
Ø: ¼-½ in (0.5-1 cm).
Cap remaining convex for a long time, yellow
ocher in dry weather, turning reddish-brown in
the wet. The gills can be seen through the
transparent cap, due to the thinness of the
flesh. Gills spaced, ocher yellow. Stipe pale yellow with silky white fibrils, a maximum of ¾ in
(2 mm) thick. Flesh very thin.

HABITAT: On mossy lawns. Summer through
fall. Very common.

SPECIAL FEATURES

Mushrooms of the Galerina genus are
difficult, if not impossible, to identify
with the naked eye.

GALERINA MARGINATA
Marginate Galera

Cap hemispherical then convex, smooth, orange-yellow when dry, brownish-ocher when wet, with a clearly striated margin. Gills cream then cinnamon. Stipe slender, often thickened at the base, ocher gray, radiated with longitudinal fibrils, and with a small ring that disappears with age. Flesh smelling strongly of flour.

HABITAT: often in large groups on the dead wood of conifers, sometimes on deciduous trees. summer through fall. Common.

DESCRIPTION: H: 1¾-3¼ in (4-8 cm), Ø: ¾-2¾ in (2-7 cm).

TOXICITY
Deadly.

GALERINA AUTUMNALIS
Autumn Galera

DESCRIPTION: H: 1½-3¾ in (3-9 cm) Ø: ¾-2¼ in (2-6 cm).
Very similar to the Marginate Galera described above, different mainly in that its cap is viscid.

HABITAT: on the dead branches of coniferous or deciduous trees. Late summer through fall. Uncommon.

TOXICITY
Deadly.

STROPHARIA AERUGINOSA

Verdigris Agaric

DESCRIPTION:
H: 2¼-4 in (6-10 cm),
Ø: 1½-3¼ in (3-8 cm).
Cap convex then
expanded, very viscid,
green or blue-green,
with shreds of white, especially around the edge. With
age, the shreds tend to disappear and
the cap takes on a pale yellow to yellow-
ocher tint. The gills are whitish at first,
then violet, but the edge remains white.
The white or blue-green stipe has much
denser white shreds than those of the cap.
It has a membranous ring, which soon
turns violet-brown from the spores. White
mycelial cords are visible at the base of the
stipe when it is uprooted. Flesh white,
bluish at the base of the stipe; practically
odorless and mild in flavor.

HABITAT: in groups in deciduous
and coniferous forests on soil rich in
organic matter,
where animals
have been and
in well-fertilized
pastures. Summer
through
fall. Very com-
mon
and widespread.

blackish fugaceous ring

mycelial cords

SPECIAL FEATURES

The Blue Agaric *(Stropharia caerulea)* is
similar but the ring is much less marked,
even in young specimens, and is often
absent. The Gills do not have a white
edge when maturie, and the cap is less
scaly.

TOXICITY

Suspected of being poisonous. This
mushroom was long considered edible
but poor, but it would be wise to avoid
eating it.

STROPHARIA SQUAMOSA, PSILOCYBE SQUAMOSA
Scaly Cap

DESCRIPTION: H:2¼-4½ in (6-12 cm), Ø:1¼-2¼ in (3-6 cm).
Cap hemispherical then convex, slightly viscid, yellowish-red or fawn, with concentric whitish scales on the margin in young specimens. Gills broad pale gray, then progressively turning violet-gray with white edges. Stipe long and slender, hollow and rigid, white with a shaggy, striated ring, edged with white scales under the ring, against a brown background. Flesh pale and smelling of humus; mild flavor.

HABITAT: on debris in deciduous forests or on leaves. Fall. Fairly common.

STROPHARIA CORONILLA
Crowned Stropharia

Cap hemispherical then convex and fleshy, pale to bright yellow or ocher, silky in dry weather, viscous when wet, margin sometimes scaly. Gills pale brown at first then violet brown, edges remaining white. Stipe sturdy, with a white, striated ring, turning brownish-black. Flesh thick and white; slight odor, mild flavor.

HABITAT: dry meadows, grazing land, fields, roadsides, clearings and edges of forests. Summer through fall. Fairly common and widespread.

DESCRIPTION: H:1¼-2 in (3-5 cm), Ø:1¼-2¼ in (3-6 cm).

STROPHARIA SEMIGLOBATA
Round Cap

DESCRIPTION: H: 1¾-4 in (4-10 cm),
Ø: ¾-1¾ in (2-4 cm).
Hemispherical then concave cap, straw-colored or yellow ocher, viscid when wet, shiny and silky when dry. Gills very broad, pale gray then violet gray, with a white edge. Stipe slender and long, hollow, rigid and brittle, slightly swollen at the base or ending in a bulb, viscid, pale yellow with a fugaceous ring quite low on the stipe which turns brown when spores fall on it. Whitish flesh, thin in the cap; odorless, mild flavor.

HABITAT: on cattle dung, and especially horse-manure in pastures. Late spring through fall. Common and widespread.

HYPHOLOMA SUBLATERITIUM
Brick Cap

DESCRIPTION: H: 2¼-8 in (6-20 cm),
Ø: 2-4 in (5-10 cm).
Cap hemispherical then convex, typically brick red at first, paler later, with a margin that is always paler and edged with white scales in young specimens. Gills crowded, whitish-yellow then violet-gray. Yellow stipe, reddening at the base and with fine scales. Flesh pale yellow, reddening in the stipe; more or less bitter flavor.

TOXICITY
Poisonous.

HABITAT: in thick tufts on old stumps of deciduous or coniferous trees. Fall. Fairly common.

HYPHOLOMA FASCICULARE
Sulfur Tuft

DESCRIPTION: H :2¼-5¼ in (6-13 cm), Ø: ¾-2¾ in (2-7 cm).
Cap globulose, soon becoming convex, then smooth and expanded, lemon yellow with a rust-colored center; the margin is thin and at first bears the remains of the yellow cortina in the form of small shreds. Later, it becomes smooth and turns pale yellowish-green. Gills are very narrow and crowded, lemon yellow but eventually grayish-green or grayish-violet. Stipe long and flexible, yellow at the top, reddish or brownish at the bottom. When spores are emitted, a grayish ring appears more or less distinctly on the upper part of the stipe. Flesh thin, bright yellow, reddish at the base of the stipe; fungal odor, very bitter flavor.

center rusty orange

POTENTIAL CONFUSION

▶ *KUEHNEROMYCES MUTABILIS*
Changing Pholiota   EDIBLE

HABITAT: Generally in very crowded tufts on dead stumps of deciduous or coniferous trees, as well as on the roots; sometimes singly or in small tufts of two or three specimens. Spring through early winter. Very common and widespread.

SPECIAL FEATURES

Sulfur Tuft is one of the commonest mushrooms, appearing with the first rains of the fall and lasting until the first frosts.

TOXICITY

Poisonous.

HYPHOLOMA CAPNOIDES
Conifer Sulfur Tuft

DESCRIPTION: H: 2¼-5¼ in (6-13 cm),
Ø: 1¼-2¼ in (3-6 cm).
This hypholoma possesses the same characteristics as Sulfur Tuft. The difference is mainly in the gills which are pale gray at first before becoming grayish-violet.They are never tinted yellow or green, and the flavor is mild.

EDIBILITY
Not very good to eat and it is advisable to avoid it due to the possibility of confusion with Sulfur Tuft.

HABITAT: in tufts on conifer stumps, mainly pine. Spring through fall and in mild winters. Fairly common, especially in the mountains.

HYPHOLOMA ELONGATUM
Long-stemmed Hypholoma

DESCRIPTION: H: 2-4¾ in (5-12 cm),
Ø: ½-¾ in (1-2 cm).
Cap convex or campanulate, then smooth and flattened,the margin slightly striated when wet, pale ocher or yellow, greenish in wet weather, ocher brown in dry weather. Gills pale yellowish then brown-violet with white edges. Stipe thin and very slender, up to 6 in (15 cm) long and ½ in (2 mm) wide, flexible, the color of the cap or paler, with a reddish-brown or orange base. Covered in white vertical fibrils, sometimes arranged in bands giving it a stripy appearance, the lower end covered in white down. Flesh thin, whitish-yellow; faint fungal odor, mild for slightly bitter flavor.

HABITAT: grows in dense clumps on moss or sphagnum moss on very damp ground. Summer through fall. Fairly common.

PSILOCYBE COPROPHILA

Coprophilous Psilocybe

DESCRIPTION: H: 2¼-2¾ in (3-4 cm),
Ø: ¼-1 in (1-2.5 cm).
Cap hemispherical or campanulate, often umbonate, ocher or
reddish-fawn, covered in a viscous, elastic and detachable film.
Gills crowded and broad, pale gray
then violet-brown. Stipe often flexible,
elastic and hollow, the same color as
the cap. Flesh thin, ocher, with faint
odor and floury taste.

HABITAT: on cattle dung in pastures in
summer and fall. Fairly
common in some
parts, and the most
widespread member
of the Psilocybe genus
in North America.

cap ocher to fawn

*brownish violet gills
darkening upon maturity*

stipe often bent

TOXICITY

Poisonous and hallucinogenic.

POTENTIAL CONFUSION

▶ *MARASMIUS OREADES*
Fairy Ring Champignon   EDIBLE

PSILOCYBE SEMILANCEATA
Liberty Caps

DESCRIPTION:
H: 2-4¾ in (5-12 cm),
Ø: ½-¾ in (1-2 cm).
Cap conical to
pointed, umbonate, not
expanding, brownish-
yellow or olive-gray,
straw or cream when
dry, covered with a
viscid film, and with
a striated margin.
Gills gray then dark
purplish-brown with
white edges. Stipe
very long and slen-
der (2-4¾ x ¹⁄₁₆ in 2-
4¾ in (5-12 cm x
0.2 cm), the same
color as the cap,
sometimes shaded
with blue-green at
the base. Flesh pale,
brownish when wet.
Slight odor of radish,
mild flavor.

SPECIAL FEATURES

Most hallucinogenic mushrooms of
species related to Liberty Caps are to be
found in the tropics, in places such as
Mexico, where they are used in religious
rites by the native peoples.

HABITAT: in groups in damp meadows, at
roadsides, on fairly acid soil. Late summer
through late fall. Uncommon.

TOXICITY

Poisonous, hallucinogenic.

KUEHNEROMYCES MUTABILIS
Changing Pholiota

DESCRIPTION: H: 1$\frac{1}{2}$-4$\frac{3}{4}$ in (4-12 cm), Ø: 1$\frac{1}{4}$-3$\frac{1}{4}$ in (3-8 cm).
Cap convex then flattened, often umbonate, smooth surface; reddish-brown when wet. The cap becomes honey-colored in dry weather, except in the center which is a different color. Very fine, transparent margin, through which the gills show. Gills slightly decurrent, yellowish, then rust-colored. Stipe often curved, striated above the ring, elsewhere covered in pointed scales or small upturned scales, beige then turned brown with the spores; faint reddish-brown ring. Flesh cream, soft in the cap, very fibrous in the stipe; odor pleasant, mild flavor.

HABITAT: in thick, dense tufts on old stumps or dead deciduous trees, especially beech, rarer on conifers. Spring through fall. Very very common.

EDIBILITY
Good to eat, pleasant fragrance. The fibrous stipe should be discarded.

POTENTIAL CONFUSION
▶ *GALERINA MARGINATA*
Marginate Galerina   DEADLY

PHOLIOTA ALNICOLA

Alder Pholiota

DESCRIPTION: H: 3¼-6 in (8-15 cm), Ø: 1¼-3¼ in (3-8 cm).
Cap convex then expanded, smooth, brilliant and viscid, bright yellow then reddish in the center, with a few shreds on the margin. Gills pale yellow becoming rust brown. Stipe undulating, fibrillose, pale yellow then reddish-brown from the base. Flesh yellow in the cap, rust at the base of the stipe; strong, pleasant, and aromatic odor, mild or slightly bitter flavor.

HABITAT: in tufts on dead or dying alder, sometimes on birches, in damp places. Summer through fall. Uncommon.

SPECIAL FEATURES

Several species of Pholiota are dedicated to particular genera of tree, for example, *Pholiota salicicola* only grows on willow.

PHOLIOTA LENTA

Glutinous Pholiota

DESCRIPTION: H: 2¼-4¾ in (6-12 cm), Ø: 1¾-3¼ in (4-8 cm).
Cap hemispherical then expanding, very viscid in wet weather, yellow, beige, or reddish, with a few white shreds at the edge of the margin on young specimens. Gills whitish-yellow, then ocher through rust brown. Stipe white, reddish toward the base, densely covered in the young specimen with white scales. White flesh, russet at the base of the stipe; mild flavor.

HABITAT: grows in small groups or only on buried branches and twigs in forests of deciduous trees, especially beech or conifers; mainly in the mountains. Fall, even late in the season. Fairly common.

SPECIAL FEATURES

The Sticky Pholiota *(Pholiota gummosa)*, is smaller and found in more open spaces; the cap is darker.

PHOLIOTA SQUARROSA
Shaggy Pholiota

DESCRIPTION: H: 4½-8 in (12-20 cm), Ø: 2-4 in (5-10 cm).
Cap hemispherical or campanulate at first, then convex and flattening, with an inrolled margin, totally covered in reddish scales with upturned tips against a yellow background, denser in the center. Gills crowded, paler then darker yellow. Stipe long, narrower toward the base, coriaceous and scaly like the cap except at the top which is yellow and smooth. Flesh thick and fibrous, yellow, smelling of celery-root, mild flavor.

HABITAT: in large tufts, on the roots of aging trees, sometimes on the stumps of deciduous and coniferous trees. Fall through early winter. Fairly common.

CONOCYBE LACTEA
Milk-white Conocybe

DESCRIPTION: H: 2-4 in (5-10 cm), Ø: ½-¾ in (1-2 cm).

Cap shaped like the finger of a glove, bell-shaped or conical, often pointed, with a striated margin, slightly viscid when wet, whitish or cream-colored, becoming pale ocher with age. Gills crowded and broad, pale ocher then bright rust-red. Stipe hollow, ¾-1¼ in (2 or 3 mm) thick, thickening at the base or with a small bulb, white and finely striated, slightly powdery at the top. Flesh very thin, fragile and white with a faint odor and bitter aftertaste.

HABITAT: lawns and roadsides. Summer through fall. Fairly common and widespread.

AGROCYBE AEGERITA, A. CYLINDRACEA

Poplar Pholiota

DESCRIPTION:
H: 3¼-6 in (8-15 cm),
Ø: 2-4 in (5-10 cm).
Cap hemispherical, then concave, flattened in older specimens, matte hazelnut to chestnut color, turning cream with age, at first at the edge. The center often remains darker; the surface is slightly wrinkled or undulating at the edge, and has a tendency to crack in the center of the cap. Gills crowded, pale, then cinnamon-colored, with white edges.

Stipe long and flexible, fibrous, pale in color, browning when the spores are deposited; ring implanted high on the stipe, well developed, and fleshy. Flesh white, except at the base of the stipe where it is brown, pleasant odor and hazelnut flavor.

HABITAT: in tufts on stumps or at the base of tree trunk along the line of the taproots, mainly on popular but sometimes on other species of deciduous trees such as the elder and even the oak. Late spring through fall, may appear several times in one year on the same stump if the weather is mild and damp. It is a warmth-loving species, fairly common in southern regions, much rarer in the north. Widespread. Highly prized in southern France and Italy.

particularly thick ring

SPECIAL FEATURES

The Poplar Pholiota has long been cultivated on a small scale in Italy, on thin slices or split logs of poplar. It can now be grown on an artificial substrate like the Oyster Mushroom or the Cultivated Mushroom.

EDIBILITY

Very good to eat, with firm, crunchy flesh tasting of hazelnut.

AGROCYBE MOLESTA, A. DURA
Tough Agrocybe

DESCRIPTION: H: 2¾-4¼ in (7-11 cm),
Ø: 2¼-4 in (6-10 cm).
Cap concave, becoming more or less flattened,
fleshy, creamy white or pale yellow, slightly viscid, slightly wrinkled or cracking with age. Gills
pale grayish then rust brown. Stipe becoming
hollow as it ages, white for long time, turning
brown from the bottom. Ring on the upper part
of the stipe, but not very consistent and disappearing very soon. Flesh thick, firm and white;
pleasant odor, slightly bitter, floury taste.

HABITAT: in troops, singly, or fused together in

twos and threes at the base of the stipe in meadows and at roadsides, on non-acidic soil. Early
summer through early fall. Uncommon but
widespread.

AGROCYBE PEDIADES
Grass Agrocybe

DESCRIPTION: H: 1¼-2 in (3-5 cm),
Ø: ¾-1¾ in (2-4 cm).
Cap hemispherical then convex, yellow
ocher, smooth. Gills widely spaced and
bowed, beige then brown with a white
edge. Stipe whitish, solid then hollow, without a ring. Flesh pale, slightly bitter or mild
and floury flavor.

HABITAT: grassland and lawns. Summer
and early fall. Fairly common in places.

SPECIAL FEATURES

The Hemispherical Agrocybe *(Agrocybe
semiorbicularis)* is similar, but has a
viscid cap. Some mycologists consider
them to be varieties of a single species.

AGROCYBE PRAECOX

Early Pholiota

DESCRIPTION: H: 3½-4¾ in (8-12 cm), Ø: ¾-2¾ in (2-7 cm).
Cap hemispherical then concave, smooth, russet to brown in wet weather, pale brown, beige or dark yellow during dry spells. Gills whitish then brown. Stipe long, thickening and sometimes bulbous at the base, whitish, with a ring very high up, which disappears quite soon, whitish but soon turning brown by being covered with spores. Flesh whitish, brownish ocher brown at the base of the stipe, odor and flavor of flour.

ring

small bulb

HABITAT: in grass at the roadsides, well-lit deciduous woods, or in parks. Late spring through early summer. Common and widespread.

PANAEOLUS FOENISECII

Harvest Paneolus

DESCRIPTION: H: 2½-3¼ in (4-8 cm), Ø: ¾-1¼ in (2-3 cm).
Cap hemispherical, soon flattening, reddish-brown, paling to pinkish-beige as it dries, often with a darker margin. Gills widely spaced, swollen, pale brown then purplish-brown, with a white edge. Stipe hollow, smooth, shiny and silky, pruinose at the top, whitish, except at the base which is reddish-brown-with white fibrils.

Flesh thin and brown; fruity odor, pleasant, and mild flavor.

HABITAT: in the grass, on lawns, on fairly rich soil. Summer through early fall. Common and widespread.

TOXICITY

Probably hallucinogenic.

PANAEOLUS SPHINCTRINUS

Sheathed Paneolus

DESCRIPTION: H: 4-6 in (10-15 cm), Ø: ¾-1¾ in (2-4 cm).

Cap ovoid then hemispherical or ogival, dark gray-brown, becoming pale gray when drying, smooth, with a dentate margin at first hung with small white shreds. Gills gray then shaded with darker and paler patches, finally completely black, except on the edge which is white. Stipe long and slender, up to 5 in (15 cm (long and only ⅛ in (2 mm) wide, and the same color as the cap, pruinose along the upper half, especially at the top. Flesh thin, pale gray; odor faint, mild flavor.

TOXICITY
Poisonous for some, inedible for others.

HABITAT: on or near cattle dung, well-fertilized meadows, and where animals have been. Early summer through fall. Fairly common and widespread.

PANAEOLUS SEMIOVATUS

Coprophilous Paneolus

DESCRIPTION: H: 2-6 in (5-15 cm), Ø: ¾-2 in (2-5 cm.

Cap campanulate or ogival, not expanding, whitish through grayish-ocher, with a darker center, surface smooth but wrinkled, shiny and silky in dry weather, viscid when wet. Gills soon becoming dark gray, with white edges. Stipe thin, perpendicular and slightly bulbous, rigid and brittle, short or very long, smooth, with a little white ring in the middle or upper third which blackens with age. Flesh white, thick in the center of the cap, thin elsewhere; faint odor, mild flavor.

HABITAT: on cow-pats or horse-dung in pastures, from late spring through fall. Quite common and widespread.

TOXICITY

Poisonous and may be hallucinogenic.

THE RUSSULALES

RUSSULA NIGRICANS
Blackening Russula

DESCRIPTION: H: 1½-4 in (4-10 cm), Ø: 2¾-8 in (7-20 cm). Cap convex and very inrolled at first, soon becoming depressed in the center, and with a margin that is inrolled for a long time, whitish or grayish from the outset, soon becoming dark gray or marbled with gray-brown. Gills widely spaced and thick, with numerous fragile gills of varying lengths, white but reddening then blackening to the touch and turning gray with age. Stipe tough, short and thick, about 2 in (5 cm) in diameter, white then darkening like the rest of the mushroom. Flesh firm, thick, white but reddening before turning black when cut, flavor mild, acrid in the gills, almost odorless, or faintly fruity odor.

HABITAT: grows under either deciduous or coniferous trees, on low and high ground. Summer through fall. Very common.

RUSSULA DENSIFOLIA

Crowded-gill Russula

DESCRIPTION: H: 2-4 in (5-10 cm),
Ø: 1¼-3¾ in (3-9 cm).
Cap convex, becoming quite deeply depressed with a very inrolled margin, often lobed with age, velvety, whitish, becoming tinged with ocher from the center. Gills very crowded, thin and narrow, of unequal lengths, pale cream then dark cream. Stipe short, 2 in (5 cm) maximum, full, pale then turning brown or red. Flesh tough and white, faintly and slowly reddening when cut, then turning gray, flavor mild or acrid.

HABITAT: under deciduous or coniferous trees, on acidic soil. Summer through fall. Common.

DESCRIPTION: H: 1¾-4 in (4-10 cm),
Ø: 2-6 in (5-15 cm).
Cap resembling that of a milk-cap, first convex then funnel-shaped, margin long remaining inrolled, often soiled with earth, creamy white

RUSSULA DELICA

Milk-white Russula

cream becoming ocher or reddish. Gills very thick and spaced, white, sometimes with bright blue tints, decurrent. Stipe short. Flesh white, unchanging, flavor mild or slightly acrid, odor fruity, becoming unpleasant in older specimens.

HABITAT: under deciduous or coniferous trees in limestone soil. Early summer, through fall. Very Common.

EDIBILITY
Very average edibility, flavor rather unpleasant.

RUSSULA OCHROLEUCA

Common Yellow Russula

cap yellow to ocher

stipe white

DESCRIPTION: H: 2¼-4 in (6-10 cm), Ø: 1¾-4 in (4-10 cm).
Cap convex at first, then flattening and becoming undulated and slightly depressed; the cuticle is smooth and shiny, easily detachable from half or two-thirds of the cap, first luminous lemon yellow, then becoming tinted with ocher or olive with age. The crowded gills are sinuated or swollen and adhere to the stipe. They are white at first but are eventually tinted pale yellow. The stipe is more or less cylindrical, often thickened at the base, solid then spongy, rough or striated. It is white in young specimens, graying progressively. The flesh is white, yellow under the cuticle, very fragile. There is no odor and the flavor is faintly acrid, but inconsistent.

HABITAT: in large groups under deciduous or coniferous trees, commoner in pine woods on sandy or acidic soil. Late summer through fall. Common.

RUSSULA CLAROFLAVA

Bright Yellow Russula

DESCRIPTION: H: 2-4½ in (5-12 cm),
Ø: 2-4¾ in (5-12 cm).
Cap convex then with a shallow depression in the center, bright yellow all over and shiny, slightly viscid in damp weather. Gills white then dirty ocher, graying to the touch. Stipe pure white slightly striated lengthwise, graying with age. Flesh white tending to gray a few minutes after cutting.

HABITAT: deciduous trees in marshy ground (mainly birch and alder), sometimes among sphagnum moss. Mainly in northern regions. Fairly common.

EDIBILITY
Quite good to eat.

RUSSULA FELLEA

Geranium-scented Russula

DESCRIPTION: H: 2¾-3½ in (4-8 cm),
Ø: 2-4 in (5-10 cm).
Cap convex but soon flattening, not very depressed, fawn orange or ocher in the center and often pale ocher at the edge. Gills the same color as the cap but paler. Stipe the same color as the gills, often swollen toward the center or at the base. Flesh white and firm, odor fruity smelling of stewed apple, flavor acrid.

HABITAT: under beech, sometimes under conifers (spruce), in the plains and mountains Fall. Common.

ocher cap

pale ocher gills and stipe

RUSSULA FOETENS
Stinking Russula

DESCRIPTION: H: 3¼-6 in (8-15 cm),
Ø: 3¼-7¼ in (8-18 cm).
Cap globulose in young specimens, then flattening and becoming depressed, viscid, with a deeply and extensively striated ocher to reddish margin, more or less spotted with darker red, thin, undulating margin, deeply fluted. Gills spaced and thick, whitish then reddish, exuding drops of liquid in young specimens. Stipe robust, tough, narrowing at the top, sometimes bulbous, white then dotted with red, full at first, then containing irregular cavities. Flesh firm and reddish, strongly rancid odor, flavor very acrid.

HABITAT: deciduous and coniferous woods. Summer through fall. Common.

RUSSULA FAGETICOLA
Beech Russula

DESCRIPTION: H: 2¼-4 in (6-10 cm),
Ø: 1½-4 in (4-10 cm).
Cap concave at first, with an inrolled margin, then becoming depressed in the center; cuticle detachable over a third of the radius of the cap at most, scarlet, discoloring in patches. Pale, crowded gills, whitish with a bluish-green tinge in young specimens. Stipe firm and solid, may be thickened at the base, white then graying at the base. Flesh tough, thick and white, pinkish under the cuticle, slightly fruity or honey odor, flavor very acrid.

HABITAT: Mainly in beech forests, sometimes under oak, on rather acidic soil, in plains and mountains. Fall. Common.

THE RUSSULALES

RUSSULA KROMBHOLZII, R. ATROPURPUREA
Black-and-purple Russula

DESCRIPTION: H: 1¾-2¾ in (4-7 cm), Ø: 2½-4 in (6-10 cm).
Cap convex then flattened and slightly

depressed in the center, fleshy and shiny, viscid in wet weather, dark purple almost black in the center, discoloring with age, margin not striated, undulating. Gills white or cream, crowded. Stipe short and cylindrical, white often maculated with ocher, graying with age. Flesh very firm, whitish, slightly acrid. Odor faint and fruity.

HABITAT: under deciduous trees (main oak) or pine trees, on grassy paths, in hollows. Summer and fall. Common.

RUSSULA FRAGILIS
Fragile Russula

DESCRIPTION: H: 1¼-2¾ in (3-7 cm), Ø: ¾-2 in (2-5 cm).
Cap convex then flattened or depressed,

viscid when wet, very variable in color, dirty pink, purple, or violet with a darker center, but the colors soon fade and the shade of the cap often tends toward greenish as it gets older. Gills white or cream, with toothed edges. Stipe white, fragile, sometimes swollen at the base. Flesh white, fairly firm, very brittle in the stipe, very acrid. flavor, fruity odor.

HABITAT: in groups in deciduous woods among birch, oak, etc., and more rarely under conifers. Late summer through fall. Very common.

RUSSULA OLIVACEA

Olive Russula

DESCRIPTION: H: 2½-6 in (7-15 cm), Ø: 3¼-7¼ in (8-18 cm.)
One of the largest russulas. Cap hemispherical then flattened with a margin that remains inrolled for a long time, sometimes with a shallow depression at the end. The surface is rough, matte, with tiny concentric wrinkles; the color is very variable, ranging from olive green shaded with purple, gray, and brown. Cuticle separable over one third of the radius of the cap. Gills crowded, butter-colored then orange. Stipe very thick 2-4½x¾-1¾- (5-12x2-4), white, often tinged with pink. Sometimes the pink is confined to circle at the top of the stipe. Flesh very firm and white, flavor mild.

HABITAT: under deciduous trees (beech, oak, etc.) or under coniferous trees in plains and mountains up to 65000 ft (2000 m) (spruce, fir). Summer through fall. Common, except in northern Europe.

TOXICITY
This Russula has been responsible for minor poisonings, especially in Italy. Once considered edible, it is now believed to be wise to refrain from eating it.

RUSSULA VINOSA
Vinous Russula

DESCRIPTION: H: 2¼-4½ in (6-12 cm), Ø: 2¼-4 in (6-10 cm).
Cap convex, soon expanded and depressed in the center, fleshy, purplish-red or dark burgundy, often darker in the center. Cuticle separable over two thirds of the radius of the cap. Gills cream or pale ocher, blackening on the margin. Stipe white, sometimes splashed with yellow toward the base, blackening with age. Flesh white, reddening then blackening in the air, with a mild flavor.

HABITAT: under coniferous trees, especially spruce, on damp or marshy ground, in the mountains. Summer through fall. Not very common.

RUSSULA INTEGRA
Entire Russula

DESCRIPTION: H: 2-4½ in (5-12 cm), Ø: 2-4½ in (5-12 cm).
Cap hemispherical at first, almost globulose, then expanded or even depressed at the end, shiny, viscous in wet weather, of variable color but generally brownish sometimes mixed with violet, purple, yellow, or green. Gills thick and well spaced, friable, white then bright yellow. Stipe up to 1¼ in (3 cm) thick, white then splashed with yellow or red. Flesh white and very firm, mild flavor.

HABITAT: in large groups in coniferous forests in the mountains. Summer through early fall. Very common.

EDIBILITY

Fairly good to eat. Not to be confused with the Bay Russula *(Russula badia)* which becomes extremely acrid after being chewed for a few moments.

RUSSULA PALUDOSA
Marsh Russula

DESCRIPTION: H: 2-6 in (5-15 cm),
Ø: 2-6 in (5-15 cm).
Cap convex then flattened, undulating or deformed, depressed, firm and shiny, slightly viscid in wet weather, blood red to pinkish-red, or orange-red. Cuticle separable over half or three-quarters of the radius of the cap. Gills cream then ocher, tinted with red on the margin. Stipe thickening toward the base or center, white or pink-tinted then more or less grayish.

HABITAT: on high, marshy ground, under conifers, especially spruce. Summer and fall. Fairly common in its habitat.

EDIBILITY
Quite good to eat.

RUSSULA XERAMPELINA, R. ERYTHROPODA
Dead-leaf Russula

DESCRIPTION: H: 2¼-4¾ in (6-12 cm),
Ø: 2¼-4¾ in (6-12 cm).
Cap convex then flattened and slightly depressed in the center, margin inrolled for a long time, very dark reddish-purple, ocher or pink, with a darkened center which can become discolored, cuticle separable over a quarter at most of the radius of the cap. Gills cream, turning ocher. Stipe 1¼ in (3 cm) thick, white tinted with pinkish red, staining brown to the touch. Flesh firm, white, browning when rubbed; odor of cooked shellfish, especially in old specimens.

EDIBILITY
Quite good to eat, but with a rather unappetizing odor.

HABITAT: conifers (pine), on acidic or siliceous soil. Late summer through fall. Very common.

RUSSULA CYANOXANTHA

Charcoal Burner

DESCRIPTION:
H: 2¼-4¾ in (6-12 cm,)
Ø: 2-6 in (5-15 cm).
Cap hemispherical then flattened and slightly depressed in the center; tough, often violet in young specimens, later becoming shaded with variety of colors— pink, purple, gray, and green—and covered in radiating fibrils. Stipe white, sometimes tinted pink, narrower at the base. Gills thick and white, flexible and not brittle, crushing to pulp under the pressure of a finger, of a greasy consistency to the touch. Flesh whitish, graying when exposed to the air, pink under the cuticle; mild hazelnut or slightly acrid flavor.

colors very variable, often mixed with gray, green, and violet

HABITAT: under deciduous trees (beech, oak, birch), sometimes under conifers. Summer through fall. Very common.

Gills white and greasy

EDIBILITY

Good to eat with a flavor like hazelnut. The Charcoal Burner is one of the tastiest russulas. Although it cannot be confused easily with a poisonous species, it is sometimes hard to differentiate it from other russulas because of the number of colors that the cap can adopt. The best test is to crush the gills with a finger, to see if they feel greasy to the touch.

RUSSULA VESCA

Edible Russula

DESCRIPTION:
H: 2¾-5¼ in (7-13 cm),
Ø: 2-4 in (5-10 cm).
Cap color very variable, but often vinous pink or reddish-brown and spotted with red marks. The cuticle often seems to be too short and does not entirely cover the margin of the cap. Gills very forked near the stipe, white spotted with small patches of rust with age. Stipe white and very firm, sometimes tinted with pink or rust. Flesh white and firm. Odor faint, not typical and mild hazelnut flavor.

HABITAT: deciduous or coniferous woods, on acidic, well-drained soil, in the plains and mountains. Late spring through fall. Very common.

EDIBILITY
Good to eat.

RUSSULA VIRESCENS

Green Cracking Russula

DESCRIPTION: H: 2-4¾ in (5-12 cm),
Ø: 2½-6 in (6-15 cm).

Cap globulose or hemispherical, then flattened and very firm, often irregular, lumpy, the margin always cracked, floury, the cuticle splits into scales which can take on a variety of colors, such as brown, ocher, and rust. Gills crowded, creamy white. Stipe thick about 2 in (5 cm) in diameter) white, sometimes slightly stained with red at the base. Flesh thick and tender, white, and with a mild hazelnut flavor, odor faint, unpleasant in the end.

HABITAT: deciduous woods (oak, beech, chestnut, birch). Fairly common in the warmer regions. late summer through fall.

EDIBILITY
Very good to eat, even raw, but the flesh is often worm-eaten.

RUSSULA LEPIDA

Pretty Russula

DESCRIPTION: H: 2¾-4 in (4-10 cm), Ø: 2¾-4¾ in (4-12 cm).

Cap identical to that of other russulas, first convex then expanded and sometimes slightly depressed; the cuticle cannot be separated from the flesh and it is velvety, matte and bright red, often discolored into pink or even yellow in places. Gills crowded, white then cream, sometimes with a pink edge. Stipe often thicker at the base where it can reach a diameter of 1¼ in (3 cm). The flesh of the cap, like that of the stipe, is extremely tough and compact; it is white, graying slightly when broken, but pink under the cuticle. The odor and flavor are quite clearly minty. Several varieties of this species are recognized.

HABITAT: mainly under beeches, as well s other deciduous trees, on any type of soil. Summer through fall. Common.

RUSSULA AURORA, R. ROSEA
Pink Russula

DESCRIPTION: H: 1¾-4¾ in (4-12 cm), Ø: 1¾-4 in (4-10 cm). Cap convex then flattened and slightly depressed in the center, pink or red. Fairly pale, often ocher in the center. Gills white and deeply forked, crowded or spaced. Stipe white and firm, pruinose at the top, swollen at the base and often narrowing just under the gills. Flesh firm and white, flavor mild and odorless.

HABITAT: under deciduous trees (beech, oak, hornbeam, etc.) or conifers, in well-drained soil. Summer through early fall. Fairly common.

EDIBILITY
Not good to eat.

RUSSULA TURCI
Turco's Russula

DESCRIPTION:
H: 1¾-4¾ in (4-8 cm), Ø: 1¾-4 in (4-10 cm). Cap convex, soon expanding with a central depression; very matte in dry weather to very viscid depending on th humidity, remaining slightly viscid in the central depression which is amethyst in color, often with a darker circle around the center. Gills

cream then fairly rapidly ocher. Stipe pure white, sometimes slightly pink in places.

EDIBILITY

Not very good to eat and the base of the stipe should be discarded.

Flesh white. Iodine odor, especially noticeable at the base of the stipe. Flavor mild.

HABITAT: under pines or other conifers, in lowlands or highlands. Summer through fall. Fairly common.

RUSSULA SANGUINARIA, R. SANGUINEA

Sanguine Russula

DESCRIPTION: H :1¾-4 in (4-10 cm), Ø: 1¾-4 in (4-10 cm). Cap fleshy, convex at first and expanding without becoming depressed, or only very slightly. The thin margin remains inrolled for a long time, the carmine cuticle pales or discolors into cream or pink scales. It looks finely granulose and dry but is slightly viscid when it rains. The gills are crowded, slightly decurrent, cream to pale ocher. The stipe is cylindrical or slightly spindle-shaped, full and firm, white or tinted with the same color as the cap, or faintly yellow, but graying upon maturity. The flesh is thick, firm and white, red under the cuticle, and with a bitter, acrid flavor.

HABITAT: under pines in the mountains, up to the tree line, and also in the lowlands. Summer through fall.

cap carmine red

stipe also stained with red

RUSSULA SARDONIA, R. DRYMEIA

Sardonyx Russula

DESCRIPTION: H: 2-4½ in (5-12 cm),
Ø: 1¾-4 in (4-10 cm).
Cap convex then flattened and slightly
depressed, sometimes umbonate, violet,
dark purple, or crimson lake, sometimes
yellowish ocher or green. Gills cream at
first then rapidly turning lemon yellow
and finally golden yellow. Stipe pruinose or
powdery, usually purple, lilac, or violet,
paler than the cap, ocher at the base,
sometimes entirely white. Odor slightly

Yellow gills

fruity, taste very
acrid. Flesh compact
and very firm, white
or lemon, pinkish
under the cuticle.

HABITAT: in large
colonies exclusively
under pine trees, in
lowland, on sandy soil.
Fall. Very common.

SPECIAL FEATURES

Mycologists identify this species without
difficulty, due to the brilliant pinkish-red
coloration it adopts in the presence of
ammonia vapor.

RUSSULA QUELETII

Quelet's Russula

DESCRIPTION: H: 2¼-4 in (6-10 cm), Ø: 1¾-3¼ in (4-8 cm).
Cap convex then depressed, slightly viscid, shiny, pinkish purple or crimson lake, with a darker center or sometimes greenish like the edge, paling to dirty ocher sale with age; cuticle separable over at least half the radius. Gills cream, faintly greenish. Stipe 2-3¼ in x ½-¾ in (5-8 cm x 1-2 cm). Fairly soft and regular, crimson lake and very pruinose, white at the very bottom. Flesh white and purplish-pink on the surface, thick and brittle, strong odor of apple or stewed apple, acrid flavor.

HABITAT: spruce, especially on limestone soil. Late summer through early fall. Very common in the mountains.

LACTARIUS PIPERATUS

Peppery Milk-cap

DESCRIPTION: H: 3¼-7¼ in (8-18 cm), Ø: 2-6 in (5-15 cm).
Cap lightly depressed in the center with a tightly inrolled margin, becoming funnel-shaped, matte creamy white, becoming stained with red. Gills very thin, crowded and narrow, white or cream. Stipe rather short, narrowing at the base. Flesh thick and white, becoming slightly greenish-yellow when broken. Abundant milk which is also white, turning pale green in one or two hours, very peppery flavor.

EDIBILITY
Not very good to eat, because it is much too peppery. Eaten raw and boiled in eastern Europe and Russia. Dried and powdered it is used as a substitute for pepper.

HABITAT: in groups or circles in damp deciduous or mixed woods. Summer and fall. Common.

LACTARIUS VELLEREUS

Fleecy Milk-cap

DESCRIPTION: H: 4-8 in (10-20 cm), Ø: 4-10 in (10-25 cm).
Similar to the Peppery Milk-cap, above, but often larger, with a velvety surface to the cap and less crowded gills.

HABITAT: under deciduous trees, mainly at the edges, in highland and lowlands., Fall. Very common.

LACTARIUS TORMINOSUS
Woolly Milk-cap

DESCRIPTION: H: 2-4 in (5-10 cm),
Ø: 2-4 in (5-10 cm).
Cap lightly depressed in the center from a young age, but very inrolled on the edge, pinkish-orange or pale orange, often with a few darker, concentric circles, and covered in a woolly fleece in young specimens. Gills creamy pink. Stipe the same color as the gills, sometimes slightly pitted. Flesh firm and white, milk white with a very acrid flavor.

HABITAT: deciduous woods, especially under birch. Summer through fall. Quite common.

LACTARIUS PYROGALUS
Burning Milk-cap

DESCRIPTION: H:2¼-4¾ in (6-12 cm), Ø:2-4 in (5-10 cm).
Cap convex or flattened, soon becoming depressed and funnel-shaped with a thin, wavy margin, almost lobed. Grayish, shaded with beige, ocher, or green, slightly viscid, sometimes with a few concentric circles. Gills slightly decurrent, widely spaced, first cream then rapidly turning luminous orange ocher. Stipe cylindrical or tapering at the base, white to gray-ish, smooth or slightly striated. Flesh white, containing an abundant white milk which turns yellow-olive upon drying. More or less fruity odor, but very persistent, acrid flavor, especially in the milk.

HABITAT: groups of varying sizes in hazelnut groves, more rarely under other deciduous trees. Late summer through fall. Common.

LACTARIUS PALLIDUS
Pale Milk-cap

DESCRIPTION: H: 2-4 in (5-10 cm), Ø: 2-6 in (5-15 cm).

Cap flattened with inrolled margin, becoming depressed fairly late, viscid, pinkish cream, beige, or ocher, almost uniform or with darker patches. Gills slightly decurrent, crowded and of unequal lengths, white then beige or yellowish. Stipe short, white, stained with red. Flesh white, then reddish in the stipe, with white, unchanging milk; flavor mild or slightly acrid.

HABITAT: mainly under beech. Late summer through fall. Quite common.

LACTARIUS SUBDULCIS
Beech Milk-cap

DESCRIPTION: H: 1¼-2¾ in (3-7 cm), Ø: 1¼-2½ in(3-6 cm).
Cap convex then flattening rapidly in the center, not very depressed but slightly umbonate, matte brown. Gills cream then reddish ocher. Stipe often curved at the base, the same color as the cap but paler at the top. Flesh pale reddish, with very abundant white milk, the flavor being mild at first, then acrid.

HABITAT: especially under beech, on clay soil. Summer through fall. Quite common.

LACTARIUS PLUMBEUS, L. NECATOR, L. TURPIS

Ugly Milk-cap

DESCRIPTION: H: 2-4 in (5-10 cm), Ø: 2-8 in (5-20 cm).
Cap convex, then with a wide, shallow depression, viscid in the center, dark olive-brown or gray-brown, margin inrolled for a long time and hairy in young specimens. Gills crowded, cream, browning at the edge and where damaged. Stipe short and thick about 1¼ in (3 cm), paler than the cap, with many small circular pits. Flesh whitish to brown, milk white and abundant, becoming gray-green as it dries. Milk and flesh taste very acrid.

HABITAT: under birch and in mixed woods containing birch on acidic soil, in lowlands and highlands.
Late summer through fall. Common.

LACTARIUS VIETUS

Gray Milk-cap

DESCRIPTION: H: 2-4 in (5-10 cm), Ø: 2-3¼ in (5-8 cm).
Cap flattened with an inrolled margin, thin, later becoming depressed in the center and with an undulating gray beige or gray violet margin. Gills cream then orange, graying with age. Stipe sometimes thicker at the base, whitish or grayish. Flesh whitish to pale red, milk white gradually turning gray-green as it dries, acrid flavor.

HABITAT: damp birch woods or pine woods, even on peaty soil. Late summer through fall. Quite common.

LACTARIUS BLENNIUS
Slimy Milk-cap

DESCRIPTION: H: 2½-4½ in (4-12 cm),
Ø: 2½-4 in (4-10 cm).
Cap convex or flattened then depressed,
very viscid when young, brown or gray-
green,with small slightly darker patches on
the edge. Gills white then staining in a few
minutes to gray-green to the touch. Stipe ¼
to ¾ in (1 to 2 cm) thick, viscid, slightly paler
than the cap. Flesh whitish,with abundant,
white, gradually turning olivaceous as it
dries, and with an acrid flavor.

*cap and stipe
viscid*

HABITAT: only under
beech. Summer
through fall. Common.

LACTARIUS TRIVIALIS
Common Milk-cap

DESCRIPTION: H: 2¼-7¼ in (6-18 cm),
Ø: 2¼-8 in (6-20 cm).
Cap large and fleshy, viscid, brownish-lilac, reddish brown or grayish-ocher, sometimes discolored. Gills slightly decurrent, cream then ocher.
Stipe slightly viscid, the same color as the cap.
Flesh compact, pale, containing an abundant
amount of milk which when it dries on the gills,
turns grayish-green, mild then acrid.

HABITAT: under conifers and birches, mainly
in the mountains in damp places. Fairly
common.

EDIBILITY

Despite its slightly acrid aftertaste, the
Common Milk-cap is sought after in certain countries in eastern Europe.

LACTARIUS SANGUIFLUUS
Bleeding Milk-cap

HABITAT: under various species of pine (Scots pine, Austrian, Aleppo pine). Fall. Common in southern regions, especially on limestone soil, but it can also be found in certain areas of northern Europe.

dark, ocher-gray cap

Gills turning dark brown when rubbed

DESCRIPTION:
H: 2-4 in (5-10 cm),
Ø: 2-4½ in (5-12 cm).
Cap not so bright as that of the Saffron Milk-cap and not marked with concentric circles. Gills ocher or reddish, but dark, staining brownish-violet when rubbed. Stipe pruinose, pinkish-orange, pitted with darker red depressions, which have a tendency to turn green like the rest of the mushroom. Flesh releases a dark red milk, which gradually turns greenish.

EDIBILITY

Very good to eat, the best of the milk-caps.

LACTARIUS DELICIOSUS

Saffron Milk-cap

DESCRIPTION: H: 1½-4 in (4-10 cm),
Ø: 2-4¾ in (5-12 cm).
Cap convex or flattened, with very inrolled
margin, becoming depressed in the center;
then the margin turns upward and the mushroom becomes funnel-shaped. Bright orange,
sometimes splashed green as it ages, with
more or less marked concentric circles. Gills
crowded and slightly decurrent, orange,
splashed with bright green where damaged.
Stipe fairly thick and hollow, also orange, dotted with small darker pits. Flesh thick and firm
in young specimens, pale
yellow to orange at
the edge, gradu-
ally becoming car-
rot -colored when
exposed to the air and exuding a
bright orange milk when broken. Odor
fruity and flavor slightly acrid.

HABITAT: in large groups, exclusively
in coniferous woods (pine) on every
type of soil, with a preference for
acidic soils. Fall.
Common.

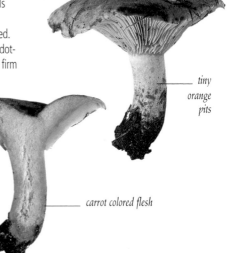

*tiny
orange
pits*

carrot colored flesh

CONFUSION

▶ *LACTARIUS DETERRIMUS*
Spruce Milk-cap   EDIBLE
▶ *LACTARIUS SALMONICOLOR*
Salmon Milk-cap   EDIBLE

LACTARIUS DETERRIMUS
Spruce Milk-cap

DESCRIPTION:
H: 2-4 in (5-10 cm),
Ø: 1¾-4½ in (4-12 cm).
It looks like the true delicious milk-cap, the Saffron
Milk-cap. How-ever, it
turns greener more
quickly and more uni-
formly. The stipe is not
pitted and has a white
mark under the gills. The
flesh turns darker red when
exposed to the air, and the
flavor is acrid.

HABITAT: only in spruce
forests, mainly in the mountains. Fall.
Common.

EDIBILITY

Edible, but with a pep-
pery taste. It is har-
vested and eaten as a
"delicious milk-cap."

LACTARIUS RUFUS
Red Milk-cap

DESCRIPTION: H: 1¾-3¼ in (4-8 cm),
Ø: 1¼-4 in (3-10 cm.)
Cap convex, soon expanding and becoming
slightly depressed, with a small umbo in the
center of the depression; uniform reddish-
chestnut or brick-red color. In young specimens, the margin is covered with a down-
coating. Gills
crowded,
decurrent,
cream then red-
dening. Stipe
slightly paler than
the cap and white
at the base. Flesh
white; abundant white milk with a very acrid
flavor , burning the lips after a few seconds.

EDIBILITY

This mushroom, which tastes horribly
acrid, is eaten in certain countries after
being specially prepared to remove the
worst of the taste.

HABITAT: coniferous woods (especially pine)
on acidic or siliceous soil. Summer through
fall. Very common.

LACTARIUS GLYCIOSMUS
Coconut Milk-cap

DESCRIPTION: H: 1¼-2¾ in (3-7 cm),
Ø: ¾-2 in (2-5 cm).
Cap convex, then slightly depressed,
sometimes with a small central umbo, velvety surface, beige to grayish-red, sometimes tinted reddish-pink or pinkish-
violet. Gills decurrent and crowded,
cream to orange, later darkening.
Flesh pale russet. White milk not very
abundant, mild or not very peppery flavor and characteristic coconut odor.

HABITAT: in groups under birch or alder,
on very damp, acidic soil. Summer through
late fall. Quite common.

LACTARIUS HELVUS
Blond Milk-cap

DESCRIPTION: H: 3¼-4½ in (8-12 cm),
Ø: 2-6 in (5-15 cm).
Cap fleshy, convex or flattened with an
inrolled margin, then depressed into a cup-
shape, sometimes with a small umbo, with a
finely granulose and downy surface, brownish-yellow or dark red. Gills decurrent, cream
in young specimens, but darkening to ocher
with age. Stipe more or less uniform or
thickening at the base, reddish orange, pruinose and often velvety at the lower end.
Flesh pale, darker at the edge, and redden-

ing when exposed to the air,. Not very abundant milk, transparent, with a mild flavor and odor of roast chicory or celery.

HABITAT: in birch woods or spruce, where there are bilberries and blueberries, bracken, and heather. It can also be found among sphagnum moss on acidic soil. Late summer through early fall. Common in the mountains.

TOXICITY
Not edible, may even be slightly poisonous.

LACTARIUS QUIETUS

Oak Milk-cap

DESCRIPTION: H: 1¾-4 in (4-10 cm), Ø: 1¾-4 in(4-10 cm).
Cap convex at first with inrolled, even margin, then slightly depressed and undulating, the surface looking as if it were covered in hoar-frost, reddish sprinkled with darker patches or with one or two darker circles Gills evenly spaced and slightly decurrent, paler and stained rust-brown where damaged. The stipe is the same color as the cap, but darker at the base. The whitish flesh turns red when exposed to the air and contains a cream-colored milk which hardly changes color. It is not very abundant, with a mild, but slightly bitter flavor and it smells of wood-lice.

HABITAT: only under oak trees and usually on acid soil. Late summer through fall. Very common.

LACTARIUS CHRYSORRHEUS

Yellow Milk-cap

DESCRIPTION: H: 2-4 in (5-10 cm), Ø: 1¾-3¼ in (4-8 cm).
Cap flattened or convex, slightly depressed in the center, pinkish-orange or pale orange, marked with patches or concentric circles of a darker color. Gills crowded, cream then orange. Stipe uneven and pruinose. Flesh turning bright yellow when broken, abundant milk turning sulfur yellow in less than a minute after breaking. Very acrid. flavor.

cap pale pinkish-yellow

TOXICITY
Poisonous.

HABITAT: deciduous woods (oak, beech, chestnut) and mixed woods. Summer though fall. Common.

LACTARIUS VOLEMUS

Abundant Milk-cap

DESCRIPTION: H:2-6 in (5-15 cm), Ø:2-6 in (5-15 cm).

Cap convex then depressed in the center, margin remaining inrolled, with a fine velvety or smooth surface, uniform color, apricot, orange, or fawn orange, sometimes darker in the center. Gills cream then splashed with brownish-ocher. Stipe the same color as the cap, yellowish at the top. Flesh firm and white, browning when exposed to air, milk abundant and white, with a mild flavor but unpleasant odor.

HABITAT: deciduous woods (beech) or under conifers. Summer and early fall. Quite common.

LACTARIUS FULVISSIMUS

Fawn Milk-cap

DESCRIPTION: H: 2¾-4 in (7-10 cm,) Ø: 2¼-3½ in (6-9 cm).
Cap becoming deeply depressed, often with a tiny central umbo, smooth or slightly granulose, reddish to orange-fawn. Fairly bright, gradually becoming paler at the margin, which is pale orange. Gills fairly crowded, becoming more separated as the cap becomes depressed, cream to pale yellow the reddish reflections, reddening with age. Stipe the same color or paler than the cap, but reddish-brown toward the base, covered in striations, which are more accentuated below the gills. Flesh pale with a strong and unpleasant rubbery odor, flavor mild but rather unpleasant, milk white, unchanging, mild or slightly acrid.

HABITAT: under deciduous trees or in mixed woods, on slightly calcareous soil. Late summer through fall. Uncommon to fairly common.

EDIBILITY
Edible, but worthless.

LACTARIUS TABIDUS
Birch Milk-cap

DESCRIPTION: H: 1½-3½ in (4-8 cm), Ø: ¾-2 in (2-5 cm).
Cap wrinkled, especially in the center, often umbonate, pale reddish ocher, darker in the center. Gills cream then orange. Stipe very brittle, the same color as the cap. Milk fairly abundant, white, yellowing in less than a minute if isolated from the flesh, flavor mild then slightly acrid.

HABITAT: deciduous or coniferous woods. Summer and fall. Common.

THE RUSSULALES

LACTARIUS HEPATICUS

Hepatic Milk-cap

DESCRIPTION: H: 2-4 in (5-10 cm), Ø: 1¼- 2¼ in (3-6 cm).
Cap convex or flattened, then depressed, liver-colored or chestnut with a hint of olive, matte, sometimes umbonate and slightly furrowed on the margin. Gills slightly decurrent, ocher with pinkish tints. Stipe the same color as the cap or reddish-brown. Flesh cream to pale red; milk abundant tending to yellow, more intensely if it is isolated from the mushroom, flavor acrid and bitter.

HABITAT: In groups under pines, on very acidic soil. Fall. Common.

LACTARIUS FULIGINOSUS

Smoky Milk-cap

DESCRIPTION: H:2-4 in (5-10 cm), Ø:1¼-3¼ in (3-8 cm).
Cap convex or flattened then slightly

depressed, not very fleshy, velvety brown, gray-ocher, brown-ocher, *café-au-lait*. Gills only slightly decurrent if at all, cream then pinkish ocher, reddening when rubbed. Stipe white, later taking on the same coloration as the cap. Flesh white becoming salmon pink in a few minutes when cut, milk abundant and white, reddening very slowly but remaining white if isolated from the mushroom. Flavor mild or acrid.

HABITAT: under deciduous trees (oak, beech, etc.) or under spruce. Summer through fall. Fairly common.

THE BOLETALES

STROBILOMYCES STROBILACEUS

Pine-cone Bolete, Old Man of the Woods

DESCRIPTION: H: 4-7¼ in (10-18 cm),
Ø: 2¾-4¾ in (7-12 cm).
Cap hemispherical then flattened,
covered in large triangular,
partially detached, grayish-
black or brownish-black
scales on a paler back-
ground; shaggy margin.
Pores large, grayish, reddening to the touch, then blackening with age. Stipe gray-brown,
woolly like the cap, except at the
top which is smooth and has a faint ring.
Flesh soft and white, turning dirty red in
contact with the air, then blackening, no
particular odor or flavor.

HABITAT: beech forests, sometimes also
under conifers, usually singly. Late summer
through early fall. Uncommon.

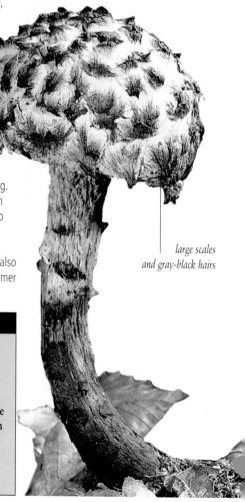

*large scales
and gray-black hairs*

TOXICITY

Suspected of being poisonous.
Some people consider it edible when
young, but of no great interest, and
when older it is too fibrous. In North
America, some cases of poisoning have
been reported, but they may have been
due to similar species found there. It is
the only bolete in Europe with this
strange shaggy appearance.

TYLOPILUS FELLEUS

Bitter Bolete

DESCRIPTION:
H: 4-7¼ in (10-18 cm),
Ø: 2-6 in (5-15 cm).
Cap hemispherical
then convex or flat-
tened, thick, yellow-
brown, pale brown,
or ochraceous-olive,
velvety texture, often
cracking in dry weather.
Pores rather wide
and angular, whitish
then pale pink with
age, turning reddish
brown to the touch.
Stipe bulbous, then
elongated and swollen
at the base, cream through ocher, decorated with a network of large, prominent
red filaments. Flesh soft in the cap and
fibrous in the stipe, white, possibly turning
slight red when exposed to the air. Pleasant odor but usually very bitter flavor.

HABITAT: under deciduous or coniferous
trees, pine and spruce on acidic, well-
drained soil. Summer through fall. Fairly
common in places.

POTENTIAL CONFUSION

▶ *BOLETUS EDULIS*
  Cep   EDIBLE
▶ *BOLETUS AESTIVALIS*
  Summer Bolete   EDIBLE
▶ *BOLETUS BADIUS*
  Bay Bolete   EDIBLE

EDIBILITY

Inedible. The bitterness, which is faint
in the raw mushroom becomes much
greater during cooking, rendering
this species inedible. One Bitter Bolete
among a collection of Ceps of Bay
Boletes, which it is easily confused with
will ruin a whole dish and make it
inedible.

BOLETINUS CAVIPES
Hollow-stemmed Bolete

DESCRIPTION: H: 2-4 in
(5-10 cm), Ø: 2-4¾ in (5-12 cm).
Cap conical and convex, then
flattened and umbonate, or on
the other hand, may be depressed
in the center, yellow-orange to reddish-brown, fibrillose or slightly scaly and
velvety, with a paler margin retaining
shreds of the original veil. Tubes curved,
decurrent to the ring, pale yellow then
olive. Pores very wide (¹⁄₁₆-⅛ in (3-4 mm),
smaller at the edge, radially elongated, yellow then olive green, stipe hollow (especially in the lower part), yellow above the
ring, the same color as the cap below it,
with a white, scaly ring.
Flesh soft and thick,
yellowish-white and
not changing color.
No characteristic
odor and flavor.

HABITAT: only
under The larch, in
the mountains. Sum-
mer through fall.
Fairly rare.

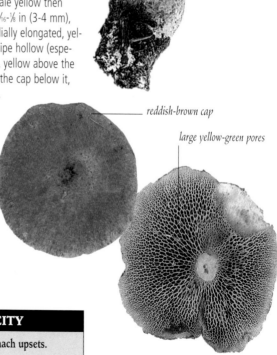

*very
large pores*

*veil leaving a ring
on the stipe*

reddish-brown cap

large yellow-green pores

TOXICITY

May have caused stomach upsets.

CHALCIPORUS PIPERATUS

Peppery Bolete

DESCRIPTION: H: 2-4 in (5-10 cm),
Ø: ¾-2¼ in (2-6 cm).
Cap convex at first then flattened, thick in the center, copper-colored, cinnamon, or reddish-brown; velvety but viscid in wet weather. Pores wide and angular, the same color as the cap, then rust or reddish. Stipe often curving, slender, tapering slightly at the base, yellow to reddish, bright yellow at the base. Flesh soon becoming soft and spongy, pink under the cuticle, pale yellow in the cap, brighter yellow in the base of the stipe. Very peppery flavor.

HABITAT: mainly under conifers (pine, larch, spruce, fir), or deciduous trees (birch, oak) especially in the mountains. Summer through fall. Fairly common.

EDIBILITY

Inedible, much too peppery. Used as a condiment in Germany and eastern Europe.

BOLETUS RADICANS, B. ALBIDUS

Rooting Bolete

DESCRIPTION: H: 4-7¼ in (10-18 cm),
Ø: 4-8 in (10-20 cm).
Cap very thick, whitish gray or beige, sometimes shaded ocher or pale brown, surface velvety at first then more or less cracked. Pores small, bright yellow then brownish-green, turning blue when touched. Stipe very thick, globulose or ovoid at first, the base ending in a point, the same color as the cap but bright lemon yellow at the top, covered in reticulation of variable color, more apparent toward the top. Flesh pale, turning blue when cut, butter flavor.

HABITAT: under deciduous trees, in parks or woods, mostly on dry, limestone soil. Summer through fall. Uncommon.

BOLETUS CALOPUS
Scarlet-stemmed Bolete

Pores small, yellow, turning green to the touch and upon maturity. Stipe cylindrical or swollen, bright red, except at the top which is yellow; decorated with a tight reticulation which is very apparent, whitish at the top of the stipe and darker toward the base. Flesh firm, creamy white or pale yellow, turning faintly blue when exposed to the air; odorless bitter flavor.

DESCRIPTION: H: 4-6 in (10-15 cm), Ø: 2¾-6 in (7-15 cm). Cap hemispherical then convex, pale, whitish-beige or *café-au-lait*, and velvety.

HABITAT: deciduous woods (oak, chestnut, etc.) or under conifers, on dry, acidic soil. Summer through fall. Fairly common or rarer, depending on the region.

BOLETUS APPENDICULATUS
Appendiculate Bolete

DESCRIPTION: H: 3¼-6 in (8-15 cm), Ø: 3¼-6 in (8-15 cm). Cap hemispherical or convex, brownish-yellow, ocher brown, or brownish-orange, with very thin crazing. Pores very small, bright yellow, faintly turning blue to the touch; tubes yellow, turning blue immediately if touched. Stipe thick and swollen, coming to a rounded point at the base, lemon yellow to dirty ocher at the base. Flesh pale yellow, may turn blue when exposed to the air, but pinkish or brownish red in the lower part of the stipe; flavor mild, pleasant fungal odor.

EDIBILITY
Very good to eat.

HABITAT: southerly, under deciduous trees, on clay and limestone soil. Summer through early fall. Uncommon.

BOLETUS EDULIS
Cep, Penny Bun Mushroom

DESCRIPTION: H: 4-10 in (10-25 cm), Ø: 2-8 in (5-20 cm).
Cap hemispherical then convex, fleshy, quite variable in color, but typically reddish-brown or hazelnut, paler at th edge, with a margin outlined in white; smooth, viscid in wet weather. The white pores turn yellow quite quickly and eventually become olive green. They do not turn blue to the touch. The stipe is full, very swollen or ovoid at first, becom-

POTENTIAL CONFUSION
▶ **TYLOPILUS FELLEUS** Bitter Bolete
▶ **BOLETUS SATANAS** Satan's Bolete   POISONOUS

ing more cylindrical as it grows and covered with a fine, white reticulation which is more obvious at the top, though it is sometime partial. Flesh white, pinkish under the cuticle, firm, softening considerably with age; flavor mild, pleasant odor.

HABITAT: sometimes singly, but usually in large colonies in coniferous woods (spruce, Scots pine, fir) and in plantations and forests of deciduous trees (oak, chestnut); commoner in mixed woods, especially on hills or at mid-mountain. On acidic, well-drained soil. Late summer through fall. Very common and widespread.

EDIBILITY
The most delicious mushroom.

BOLETUS AESTIVALIS

Summer Bolete

YDESCRIPTION: H: 3¼-8 in (8-20 cm), Ø: 2-6 in (5-15 cm).
Cap hemispherical then convex, uniform in color, orange-brown or pale fawn, with a dry, almost velvety, cuticle, often finely

POTENTIAL CONFUSION

▶ *TYLOPILUS FELLEUS*
Bitter Bolete

EDIBILITY

Very good to eat, but often worm-eaten, and less highly prized than the Cep.

cracked, and not viscid when wet. Pores white, tending later to yellow then olive-green. Stipe solid and firm, slightly swollen, tinged with ocher or brownish-orange, with a clearly-marked reticulation over the upper half of the stipe. Flesh firm, soon becoming soft, white under the cuticle; pleasant odor, sweet, mild flavor.

HABITAT: well-lit woods and the edges of deciduous woods (oak, beech, chestnut, etc). May through early fall in lowlands and highlands. Common and widespread.

BOLETUS AEREUS
Black-headed Bolete

often reveal the white flesh underneath. Pores milk-white at first, bulbous stipe narrowing at the top, ocher or rusty brown with a faint reticulation, white then turning brown. Flesh very firm, white, even under the cuticle, pleasant odor, mild flavor.

HABITAT: well-lit forests, verges, and only under deciduous trees, especially oak. Summer through early fall. Fairly common in southern Europe, and on France's Atlantic coast but in warm years it can be found further north.

sepia-colored velvety cap

DESCRIPTION :
H: 4-6 in (10-15 cm),
Ø: 2-7¼ in (5-18 cm).
Cap hemispherical and fleshy, firm in young specimens, sepia, chocolate, or almost black in color, matte and velvety, sometimes becoming marbled or veined with ocher or brick-red tints. Animal bites

EDIBILITY

Delicious, some even prefer it to the cep, but the flesh softens considerably with age, so only young specimens are good.

SPECIAL FEATURES

Several other species of bolete which are mistaken for the black-headed bolete because the color of their caps may vary and become very dark. This is the case, for instance with Pine Boletes and Ceps that grow under chestnut trees.

BOLETUS PINOPHILUS
Pine Bolete

DESCRIPTION: H: 10-20 cm, Ø : 6-18 cm. Cap very fleshy and hemispherical, smooth but often slightly lumpy, pinkish-red, reddish-brown, or mahogany, and matte. Pores white at first, then yellow-green. Stipe very swollen, white at the top, but tinted ocher or mahogany at the bottom, with fine white reticulation at the top. Flesh compact and white, reddish-brown under the cuticle; odor slightly resinous, mild flavor.

HABITAT: often singly in forests of conifers, mainly Scots pine, as well as spruce, fir and mixed forest, usually on high ground, on acid or sandy soil. Summer through fall. Fairly common in the south, rarer in the north; widespread.

EDIBILITY
Edible and delicious.

BOLETUS SATANAS
Devil's Bolete

DESCRIPTION: H: 8 in (10-20 cm,) Ø: 4-10 in (10-25 cm).
Cap hemispherical, then convex and undulating, very fleshy, dirty white, ash gray, cream, pale brown or olive, graying with age. Pores bright yellow at first then rapidly

TOXICITY
Poisonous, especially when raw; causes gastro-enteritis attacks which manifest some hours later by violent and repeated vomiting.

turning orange or brick-red, paler at the margin, tending to turn blue-black when touched; tubes yellow then olive-green. stipe very swollen and short, extending later, yellow at the top and often at the base as well, red in the middle, with an orange or red reticulation over the whole of

POTENTIAL CONFUSION

▶ ***BOLETUS EDULIS***
Cep   EDIBLE
▶ ***BOLETUS ERYTHROPUS***
Red-stemmed Bolete   EDIBLE

SPECIAL FEATURES

Many red-pored boletes are more or less poisonous, including the Red-stemmed Bolete which is only edible if well cooked. Furthermore, many of these boletes are hard to identify. For this reason, it is a good idea to avoid eating any boletes with red pores.

the top. Flesh white or pale yellow , turning faintly blue when exposed to the air ; faint odor, becoming more unpleasant with age, mild flavor.

HABITAT: clearings, verges and well-lit deciduous woods (mostly oak and beech), on limestone soil. Fairly common in the south, rarer in the north, and in warm, sun-lit places. Reoccurs in the same places. Fall.

grayish-white cap   *top of stipe yellow*   *red pores*

stipe densely covered in red spots

BOLETUS ERYTHROPUS
Red-stemmed Bolete

SPECIAL FEATURES

Often mistaken for the Devil's Bolete. The flesh of many boletes, including the edible ones, turns blue when exposed to air, a phenomenon of oxidation. The Red-stemmed Bolete is edible and good to eat, unlike the Devil's Bolete (*Boletus Satanus*) which is poisonous whether raw or cooked.

Flesh firm, bright yellow but turning dark blue a few seconds after it is cut, eventually fading to the original yellow color; untypical odor, mild flavor.

DESCRIPTION: H: 3¼-8 in (8-20 cm), Ø: 2¾-7¾ in (7-18 cm). Cap hemispherical then convex and flattened, dark chestnut, sometimes reddish-brown or olivaceous ocher, typically velvety. Pores small and dark red, turning more orange with age, yellow-orange on the margin, becoming dark blue immediately when touched. Stipe cylindrical or often swollen at the base, not reticulated but densely covered with little bright red spots, aligned more or less vertically, against a yellow background.

HABITAT: verges, clearings, and well-lit forests of deciduous trees, rarer under conifers; on acidic, well-drained soil, in highlands and lowlands. Common and widespread.

POTENTIAL CONFUSION

▶ *BOLETUS SATANAS*
Devil's Bolete   POISONOUS

EDIBILITY/TOXICITY

Poisonous raw, good to eat when cooked.

BOLETUS LURIDUS

Lurid Bolete

DESCRIPTION: H: 4-8 in (10-20 cm), Ø: 3¼-7¼ in (8-18 cm).
Cap hemispherical then convex, variable in color, ocher, yellow-brown, orange-brown, or olive, with a velvety surface. Tubes yellow then green, turning blue when cut. Pores yellow, soon turning reddish-orange, but turning blue to the touch. Club-shaped stipe, yellow at the top, reddish-orange elsewhere, purplish-red at the base of the stipe, covered in a tick, elongated blood-red reticulation. Flesh firm at first, yellow in the cap and the top of the stipe, dark red in the base of the stipe, turning brightly blue when cut. The tubes and flesh of the cap are separated by a red line; pleasant odor and mild flavor.

HABITAT: well-lit mixed or deciduous forests on limestone. soil in early summer through fall. Fairly common and widespread.

EDIBILITY

Considered to be very good to eat, but may have caused some intestinal upsets.

BOLETUS PULVERULENTUS
Powdery Bolete

DESCRIPTION:
H: 2-4¾ in (5-12 cm),
Ø: 1¾-4 in (4-10 cm).
Cap hemispherical then convex, flattened at the center or slightly depressed, velvety, very variable in color from café-au-lait, ocher, chocolate brown, reddish or pink, becoming stained blue-black to the touch. Pores bright yellow, then olive, turning dark blue when touched, stipe thinning toward the base, yellow and powdery

on top, striated or punctuated with red toward the bottom. Flesh yellow, instantly turning bright blue when cut, then blackening; pleasant odor and flavor.

HABITAT: deciduous (oak) or coniferous woods, beside forest paths, in parks and avenues. Prefers limestone soil. Summer through fall. Uncommon.

XEROCOMUS PARASITICUS
Parasitic Bolete

DESCRIPTION: H: 1½-3¼ in (4-8 cm),
Ø: 1¾-4 in (2-5 cm).
Cap hemispherical then convex, slightly velvety and cracking on the surface, ocher yellow to brownish-olive. Pores coarse and angular, ocher yellow, turning rust colored, but not blueing. Stipe smooth and fibrillose, often curved at the base, reddish-brown or yellow-brown. Flesh thick and pale, not reddening when cut; flavor mild, odor pleasant.

HABITAT: Parasitic on the Common Earthball (*Scleroderma*

citrinum). It grows in groups of two or three at the base of the Earth-ball, on very humid soils. Summer through fall. Fairly rare but widespread.

XEROCOMUS CHRYSENTERON
Red-cracking Bolete

DESCRIPTION: H: 2-4 in (5-10 cm), Ø:2-4 in (5-10 cm).
Cap hemispherical then convex, varying in color from grayish-yellow through brownish-green, reddish-brown, velvety at first, then cracking to reveal reddish flesh. Bites of small animals are also edged with red. Pores large, angular, yellow then olive-green, turning faintly blue to the touch. Stipe often sinuous, fairly thin, may be expanded or thinning at the base, yellow at the top, more or less striated with red elsewhere. Flesh soft, lemon yellow, pinkish-red under the cuticle, turning faintly blue when cut; pleasant odor and flavor.

HABITAT: singly or in large groups in deciduous or coniferous woods, on acidic or siliceous soil. Summer through fall. Very common and widespread.

EDIBILITY
Edible but mediocre, not fleshy and with soft flesh.

flesh vinous red between the cracks

olive-green pores

XEROCOMUS SUBTOMENTOSUS

Downy Bolete

DESCRIPTION: H: 2¾-6 in (7-15 cm)
Ø: 2-6¾ in (5-12 cm).
Cap hemispherical then convex, *café-au-lait*, ocher olive, and with the texture of chamois leather. Pores wide, especially near the stipe, irregular and angular, golden yellow, eventually turning green, and faintly blue to the touch. Stipe often curved, thin or sturdy, thickening at the base, can be as long as 6 in (15 cm), yellow, covered in coarse reddish-brown striations which sometimes combine into a vague network at the top. Flesh thick, white or pale yellow, not turning blue; pleasant odor, mild flavor.

HABITAT: woods and borders of deciduous or coniferous woods, soften with the Red-cracking Bolete, on non-calcareous soil. Summer through fall. Fairly common and widespread.

SPECIAL FEATURES

Species very similar to the Red-cracking Bolete (*Xerocomus chrysenteron*) and Bay Bolete (*Xerocomus badius*), of which there are various intermediate forms.

XEROCOMUS BADIUS
Bay Bolete

DESCRIPTION: H: 2½-4¾ in (6-12 cm), Ø: 2-6 in (5-15 cm).
Cap fleshy, hemispherical then flattened , viscid in damp weather, velvety in dry weather, uniform in color, bay (chestnut) to reddish-brown. Pores lemon yellow then olive, instantly staining dark blue-green when touched. Stipe irregular, thickened or thinning, narrower or otherwise at the base, ocher or reddish-brown all over, but striated vertically with reddish-brown and not reticulated. Flesh thick, soft in the cap, whitish-yellow, turning faintly blue when cut, pleasant fungal odor, mild flavor.

HABITAT: mainly in coniferous forests, sometimes under deciduous trees (oak, beech, chestnut), or in clefts in stumps; on acid soil. Occasionally in summer, but mainly in fall. Very common, widespread throughout the temperate northern hemisphere.

bay brown cap

striated stipe

pores yellow, turning bluish-green to the touch

EDIBILITY

Very good to eat and rarely worm-eaten, often growing in large numbers. The tough stipe should be discarded.

SPECIAL FEATURES

The Bay Bolete is one of the few boletes which does not form mycorrhiza with tree roots.

LECCINUM AURANTIACUM

Orange Bolete

DESCRIPTION: H: 4¾-8 in (12-20 cm), Ø: 4-8 in (10-20 cm).
Cap globulose or hemispherical at first, barely wider than the stipe, then expanding and enlarging until it is convex, with a velvety cuticle which overlaps the margin, and is uniformly reddish-orange, sometimes brownish-orange. Pores small, white, turn-

ing gray-brown with age. Stipe tough, slightly swollen toward the base, covered in small rusty or reddish-brown, granulose scales. Flesh thick, firm in the stipe, softening with age in the cap, whitish when cut, turning dirty pink and finally violet-black; pleasant odor mild and pleasant flavor.

HABITAT: under birch, aspen, and poplar on damp, clay soil. Summer through fall. Fairly common in the northern hemisphere.

LECCINUM QUERCINUM

Oak Bolete

DESCRIPTION: H: 6¾-8 in (12-20 cm, Ø: 2½-6¾ in (6-18 cm).
Cap hemispherical then convex, velvety when dry, soft finely cracked on the margin, brick-red or brownish-orange, browning with age. Pores fine, whitish, pale ocher subsequently, slightly browning to the touch. Stipe slightly thickened at the base, white, covered in small reddish scales which later turns brown, flesh firm then spongy, white, turning pink or gray when cut, sometimes blue-green at the base of the stipe; pleasant odor, mild flavor.

HABITAT: under oak, chestnut, and occasionally under beech. Summer through fall. Uncommon.

SPECIAL FEATURES

This species is often confused with the Orange Bolete which grows under deciduous, water-loving trees such as aspen and poplar.

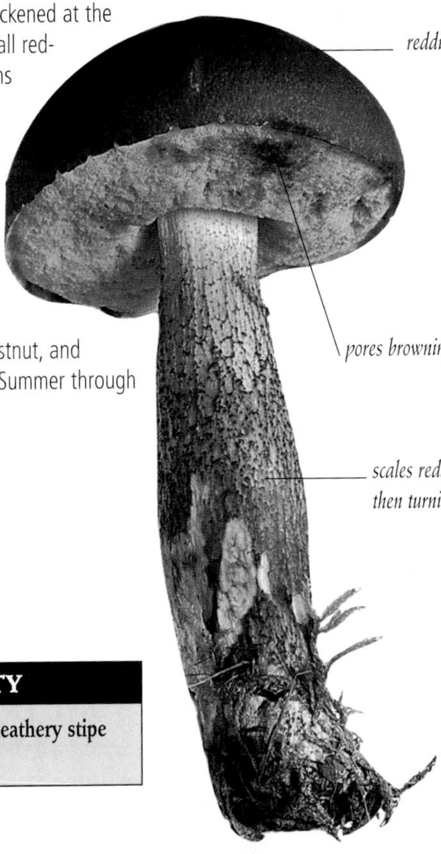

reddish-brown cap

pores browning to the touch

scales reddening then turning brown

EDIBILITY

Quite good to eat, if the leathery stipe is discarded.

LECCINUM SCABRUM
Brown Birch Bolete

DESCRIPTION: H: 4-10 in (10-25 cm),
Ø: 2-6 in (5-15 cm).

Cap hemi-spherical then convex, hazelnut, gray-brown or brownish-yellow, slightly velvety when dry, viscid when wet. Pores white at first, then turning gray, browning to the touch. Stipe long, widening from top to bottom, whitish but covered with little grayish-black, crowded spots. Flesh soft in the cap, fibrous in the stipe, white, not blackening; odor pleasant, flavor mild.

HABITAT: under birch and in mixed woods containing birch, on damp, acidic soil. Summer through fall. Very common.

EDIBILITY

Edible but mediocre, flesh soft and without much flavor.

SPECIAL FEATURES

This is a collective species, a group of which the various varieties are some-times hard to distinguish, and which were once collected under the botanical name of *Boletus scaber*.

LECCINUM CARPINUM

Hornbeam Bolete

DESCRIPTION: H: 4-7¼ in (10-18 cm),
Ø: 2-4 in (5-10 cm).
Cap hemispherical then convex, pitted,
sometimes cracking in dry weather and

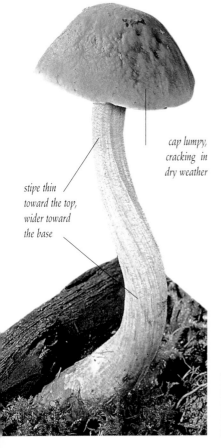

cap lumpy, cracking in dry weather

stipe thin toward the top, wider toward the base

with age, fairly soft, hazelnut or brownish-
yellow, shaded ocher or fawn. Pores small
and white, then dirty yellow and eventually
turning gray. Stipe slender toward the top,
becoming progressively wider toward the
base and very scaly. The little gray scales
covering a paler background are aligned
vertically, giving the stipe a striated look.
Flesh firm in the stipe, soft in the cap; white
when cut but instantly changing to dark
pink then to violet-black. Odor faint but
pleasant, flavor mild, slightly acidic.

HABITAT: under hornbeam, hazelnut, or
oak, on cool, shady soil. On highland or
lowland. Summer through fall. Common.

EDIBILITY

Edible but mediocre, the soft flesh blackens when cooked.

LECCINUM DURIUSCULUM

Poplar Bolete

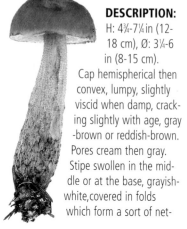

DESCRIPTION:
H: 4¾-7¼ in (12-18 cm), Ø: 3¼-6 in (8-15 cm).
Cap hemispherical then convex, lumpy, slightly viscid when damp, cracking slightly with age, gray-brown or reddish-brown. Pores cream then gray. Stipe swollen in the middle or at the base, grayish-white, covered in folds which form a sort of network, and very densely dotted with fine brown scales. Flesh firm and white, reddening at the top of the stipe when cut, turning blue at the bottom, and finally blackening.

HABITAT: under poplar or aspen, in forests, beside waterways. Fall. Uncommon.

EDIBILITY
Quite good to eat when young.

SUILLUS AMERICANUS

American Bolete

DESCRIPTION: H: 1¾-4 in (4-10 cm), Ø: 1¼-4 in (3-10 cm).
Cap convex, with an inrolled margin covered in yellowish, viscid hairs. Brilliant yellow, spotted or striped with red. Pores wide and angular, even elongated, yellow then ocher, covered in young specimens with a yellowish veil, which leaves no ring since it is not attached to the stipe. Stipe thin for a Bolete (less than ½ in (1 cm)), yellow, spotted at the top, the spots darkening with age. Flesh yellowish, turning reddish-brown when cut.

HABITAT: only under pines. Summer and early fall. Very common in North America.

EDIBILITY
Good to eat.

SUILLUS BOVINUS

Bovine Bolete

DESCRIPTION: H: 2¾-3¼ in (4-8 cm), Ø: 2-4 in (5-10 cm).
Cap convex then flattened and lumpy, thick at the center, with a thin margin, ocher or orange, shiny, viscid in damp weather. Pores large, especially close to the stipe, elongated and more or less aligned with the stipe, composite (divided into several compartments), yellow-green, browning to the touch. Stipe slender, often flexed, ocher, covered in reddish fibrils as it ages and sometimes with pink filaments of reddish-orange mycelium attached to the base. Flesh soft and elastic, whitish-yellow; Pleasant odor, mild flavor.

HABITAT in groups, only under pines, in forests or heaths on acidic soil, on highland or lowland. Late summer through fall. Found all over the world.

EDIBILITY

Edible but mediocre with flabby flesh.

SUILLUS VARIEGATUS

Speckled Bolete

DESCRIPTION: H: 2¹/₄-4³/₄ in (6-12 cm), Ø: 2¹/₄-6 in (6-15 cm).

Cap hemispherical then flattened with a thin margin, yellow ocher, orange, or brownish-yellow, later turning olivaceous. Velvety at first then finely granulose, slightly viscid in wet weather. Pores small and angular, yellowish then brownish-green, turning

SPECIAL FEATURES

This and the Speckled Bolete are the only species of *Suillus* growing under pine whose stipe has no ring or granulation.

faintly blue to the touch. Stipe long and sturdy, yellowish. Flesh firm, rapidly softening, pale yellow, faintly blueing, when cut; faint odor of bleach, mild but unpleasant flavor.

HABITAT: coniferous woods, especially pine, in the mountains, mainly on acidic or sandy soil. Late summer through fall. Common.

SUILLUS GRANULATUS
Yellow Pine Bolete

DESCRIPTION: H: 3¼-5 in (8-15 cm), Ø: 2-4¾ in (5-12 cm).
Cap hemispherical or conical then convex, yellowish-orange to reddish-brown, uniform, very viscid when wet, silky and matte in dry weather, with a cuticle that overlaps the margin and is easily detachable. Pores small, successively pale yellow, bright yellow, and finally reddish, exuding milky drops in young specimens. Stipe solid and firm, white or pale yellow; the top exudes the same milky drops as the pores, later presenting red dish or brownish granulations. Flesh thick, white or yellow, unchanging when cut. Spicy odor and flavor.

HABITAT: in groups, only under pines (Scots pine, Austrian pine, Aleppo pine, etc.), often in the grass and prefers limestone soil. In lowland and highland. Late summer through fall. Very common along the European Atlantic coast, less so elswhere.

chair yellow bright

pores yellow then reddening

EDIBILITY

Good to eat, although it tends to be indigestible. The viscid, bitter cuticle must be discarded before preparation.

SUILLUS LUTEUS
Slippery Jack

DESCRIPTION: H: 2¾-7¼ in (7-13 cm),
Ø: 2-6¾ in (5-12 cm).
Cap convex, expanding very late, very
viscid and sticky, mostly chocolate
brown in color, sometimes reddish-
brown or ocher, with thin, darker stripes;
tiny shreds of the white veil are attached
to the margin, and the cuticle is easily separable. Pores small and rounded, lemon yellow, turning green with age. Stipe fairly
short, thick and sturdy, sometimes bent,

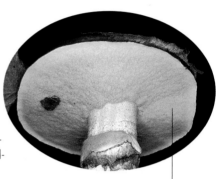

small lemon yellow pores

cylindrical and
slightly thickened at the
base, firm and fibrous,
white to yellow, with
tiny reddish granula-
tions at the top, and
with a wide membra-
nous ring, white then
violet-brown. Flesh
thick, firm at first then
becoming soft, whitish
to pale yellow, and yel-
lower in the base of
the stipe; pleasant
odor, mild flavor.

EDIBILITY

Good to eat, and considered to be the
best of the *Suillus*, as long as the slimy,
bitter cuticle is first discarded, and only
young specimens are eaten.

HABITAT: in groups, only under pines,
mainly Scots pine, in the grass, at roadsides, and beside ditches. Fall. Common
throughout the Northern Hemisphere,
especially in warmer parts.

SUILLUS GREVILLEI
Larch Bolete

DESCRIPTION: H: 2¾-6 in (6-15 cm), Ø: 2-4 in (5-10 cm).
Cap hemispherical then convex or flattened, bright lemon yellow to orange-yellow, very shiny and viscid. Pores hidden by a woolly white veil in young specimens, lemon yellow, turning reddish or pinkish gray to the touch. Stipe often slightly swollen at the base, uniform yellow below the ring and with reddish veins above it. The ring is whitish and woolly, forming a ridge. Flesh pale yellow in the cap, bright yellow in the stipe, veined with violet when cut; pleasant odor and flavor.

HABITAT: only under larch in parks and plantations, in avenues among the grass, sometimes quite far from the tree, in highlands and lowlands. Summer through fall. Fairly common.

EDIBILITY
Edible but mediocre. The slimy cuticle should be discarded.

SUILLUS VISCIDUS

Slippery Larch Bolete

DESCRIPTION: H: 2¾-6 in (7-15 cm), Ø: 2-4 in (5-10 cm).

Cap hemispherical then convex or flattened, extremely viscid, surface slightly wrinkled, beige then gray-brown, turning greenish-gray with age; the edge sometimes retains the remains of the whitish veil in the form of small shreds. The pores are large, irregular, pale, then turning brown or grayish-green. The stipe is whitish or yellowish above the ring, dirty red or brown below it; the ring is wide and white at first, then flattened against the stem and browning. The flesh is soft, whitish, turning gray or brown in places when cut. The odor is faint and flavor mild.

HABITAT: only under larch, whether wild or cultivated, in lowlands and highlands. Prefers limestone soil. Early summer through fall. Commoner in the mountains.

EDIBILITY

Edible but very poor eating, as the flesh is soft and spongy.

GOMPHIDIUS GLUTINOSUS

Glutinous Gomphidius

decurrent gills

completely separable from the cap. Gills broad, widely spaced, decurrent, more or less forked, of a waxy consistency, whitish then blackish, very easily separated from the rest of the cap. Stipe not very thick at the base, very viscid, white except at the base which is lemon yellow and with a small ring of brown scales. Flesh thick only at the center of the cap, white, bright yellow at the base of the stipe; odorless, mild in flavor.

HABITAT: coniferous forests (spruce in the mountains, pines in the lowlands) especially at the edge of the woods. Summer through fall. Fairly common and widespread.

DESCRIPTION: H: 2¾-5¼ in (7-13 cm), Ø: 2-4 in (5-10 cm).
Cap conical and umbonate, then with a flattened top, becoming funnel-shaped with age, covered with a thick, gelatinous film; the margin remains inrolled for a long time and is attached to the stipe by a glutinous veil in young specimens, which is *café-au-lait*, gray-violet, then reddish-brown in color, staining black when touched. The cuticle is easily

EDIBILITY

Good to eat, as long as the viscid cuticle is removed, but the flesh blackens during cooking.

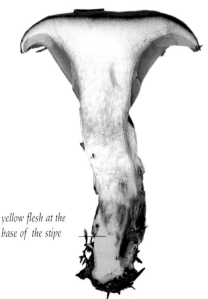

yellow flesh at the base of the stipe

CHROOGOMPHUS RUTILUS, GOMPHIDIUS VISCIDUS

Coppery Gomphidius

Flesh orange-yellow with a tendency to redden, odorless and with a mild flavor.

HABITAT: under conifers, very often pines, rarer under spruce; sometimes even around individual trees in hedgerows or meadows. Late summer through fall. Fairly common and widespread.

DESCRIPTION: H: 2¾-6 in (7-15 cm), Ø: 2-4 in (5-10 cm).
Cap conical, sometimes becoming umbonate, the margin remaining inrolled, viscid, copper-colored, reddish-brown or dark red, paler as it ages. Gills very widely spaced and decurrent, easily detachable from the rest of the cap, reddish-ocher then dark brown with age. Stipe often long, generally thinner at the top or bottom and swollen toward the middle, marked with reddish zones or covered with small scales flattened against it.

EDIBILITY

Edible but mediocre, not as popular as the Glutinous Gomphidius.

PAXILLUS INVOLUTUS
Brown Roll-rim

DESCRIPTION: H: 2¾-4¾ in (6-12 cm), Ø: 2-6 in (5-15 cm).
Cap convex at first but soon becoming depressed in the center, sometimes umbonate, with a margin which remains inrolled for a long time, more or less fluted; surface velvety or cracked in dry weather, viscid in wet weather, cinnamon or brownish-ocher. Gills very crowded, narrow, and decurrent, very forked, beige then rust, gradually turning brown to the touch, until they become dark brown some minutes later. Stipe central or slightly excentric, fibrillose, of the same color as the cap, staining brown when touched. Flesh thick and soft, pale yellow or pale brown, browning when exposed to the air as well as when rubbed. Fruity odor, slightly bitter flavor.

HABITAT: under deciduous trees, especially birch, but also chestnut, poplar, or under conifers in the mountains, in parks, on lawns, on the ground or on old, rotting stumps, on damp, acidic soil, from early summer through late fall. Extremely common and widespread.

reddish, crowded gills

TOXICITY

The Brown Roll-rim used to be considered edible, but it has caused serious cases of poisoning, some of them fatal. It is more poisonous when raw.

PAXILLUS ATROTOMENTOSUS

Black-stemmed Roll-rim

DESCRIPTION: H: 2¼-7¾ in (6-18 cm), Ø: 4-10 in (10-25 cm).
Cap convex then funnel-shaped, kidney- or shell-shaped, the margin remaining inrolled for a long time, brownish-ocher or brownish-yellow,velvety then more or less fissured. Gills crowded, decurrent, branched, bonded together at the base, easily separable from the rest of the cap, cream to yellow, browning to the touch. Stipe short and thick, often excentric, covered with a very dense brownish-black down.Flesh soft and spongy, white to pale yellow, brown in the stipe; odorless, flavor more or less bitter.

HABITAT: in tufts on conifer stumps or roots. Summer through early fall. Uncommon.

TOXICITY
May be poisonous.

OMPHALOTUS ILLUDENS
Deceiving Funnel-cap

DESCRIPTION: H: 3¼-7¾ in (8-18 cm, Ø: 2¼-6 in (6-15 cm).
Cap slightly convex at first, with very inrolled margin, then depressed in the center but retaining its inrolled margin. Surface smooth and matte, may become very slightly scaly at the center, egg-yellow to orange-yellow or apricot. Gills very crowded, thin, decurrent, of the same color as the cap. Stipe pale yellow, spindle-shaped, ending in a point at the base and fused with the stipes of other specimens, from which it is easily separable. Flesh firm, fibrous in the stipe; fairly strong and unpleasant odor, similar to that produced by the Clouded Agaric (*Clitocybe nebularis*).

HABITAT: forms dense and voluminous tufts on old logs of various deciduous trees, especially oak. Often grows on roots or buried stumps. Summer through fall. Uncommon, probably originates from North America, but also found in Europe.

POTENTIAL CONFUSION

▶ *CANTHARELLUS CIBARIUS*
Chanterelle   EDIBLE

▶ *HYGROPHOROPSIS AURANTIACA*
False Chanterelle   EDIBLE

TOXICITY
Poisonous.

OMPHALOTUS OLEARIUS
Jack O'Lantern

DESCRIPTION: H: 2¾-6 in (7-15 cm), Ø: 2½-4¾ in (6-12 cm).
Cap convex then becoming depressed in the center, and finally funnel-shaped but retaining a more or less inrolled margin, yellow orange to brownish-orange. Shiny, very decurrent gills, yellow-orange, thin, and crowded, easily separable from the cap. Stipe long, undulating, often excentric, striated, the same color as the cap, stained brownish-gray. Flesh very fibrous, bright yellow.

HABITAT: in tufts at the base of tree trunks, on the branches of deciduous trees or on the ground, growing on buried roots. Summer through fall. Quite common in the south.

POTENTIAL CONFUSION
▶ *CANTHARELLUS CIBARIUS*
Chanterelle   EDIBLE

TOXICITY
Very poisonous.

HYGROPHOROPSIS AURANTIACA

False Chanterelle

DESCRIPTION: H: 1¼-2½ in (3-6 cm), Ø: 1¼-2¾ in (3-7 cm).
Cap convex but soon depressed in the center, margin inrolled for a long time, funnel-shaped with age, edge slightly undulating; yellow-orange to reddish-orange, sometimes darker in the center. Gills crowded, decurrent, very forked, reddish-orange. Stipe thin and narrower at the base, smooth and coriaceous, becoming hollow, dark orange-red at the base; chair flaccid and elastic, no particular odor or flavor.

HABITAT: in groups in coniferous forests, especially pine, sometimes spruce, on the ground or on very rotten, buried branches. Late summer through fall. Common and widespread.

EDIBILITY
Wrongly accused of being poisonous. In fact, it is quite good to eat though the flesh is rather soft.

THE GASTEROMYCETES

GEASTRUM SESSILE
Sessile Earth Star

DESCRIPTION:
Ø: 1½-2 in (3-5 cm).
The Sessile Earth Star consists of an outer segmented part and a spherical central part. The outer part consists of six to nine smooth triangular segments, creamy-white to ocher in color. In wet weather they are stretched out parallel to the earth and in dry weather they are incurved, raising the central part up from the ground. The spherical center is the same color as the segments, or slightly darker, grayish ocher. Their consistency is similar to that of wasps' nests or parchment. The top is perforated with a little hole with an irregular, toothed edge. The flesh is coriaceous and has no particular odor.

HABITAT: Often in colonies, on moss or needles in coniferous or mixed forests. Summer and early fall. Widespread.

GEASTRUM TRIPLEX

Triple Earth Star

DESCRIPTION: H: ¾-2 in (2-5 cm), Ø: 1½-2 in (3-5 cm) (closed), 2¼-(6-12 cm) (open). In its young state, the fungus is ovoid and subterranean. It develops in a spherical form in two parts, an external part which splits into five to seven segments, cream then turning gray, about ⅛ in (0.5 cm) thick, which expands and wraps itself underneath the fungus, becoming split crosswise. The central part is globulose and opens at the top in a tiny star-shaped opening, surrounded by a white circle, from which the spores are emitted.

SPECIAL FEATURES

Geasters are strange fungi whose botanical name means "earth star."

HABITAT: Deciduous or coniferous forests, parks. Fall. Uncommon.

ASTRAEUS HYGROMETRICUS

Hygrometric Earth Star

DESCRIPTION: Ø: ¾-4 in (2-10 cm). The fungus consists of two parts, the central globulose part about 1 in (2.5 cm) in diameter which is pale gray, and pierced at the top with a small orifice, and the outer part which is brown to ocher, forming a six to ten branched star (sometimes there are even more branches). The branches are fused at the base, and the surface is cracked. When the air becomes too dry, the branches fold back into the center, enclosing the globe. Flesh brown at maturity.

HABITAT: clearings, hedgerows, deciduous (oak) or coniferous (pine) trees, on sandy, rather acidic soil. Late summer through early fall, but may persist for several months in the dry state. Widespread but uncommon.

LYCOPERDON PYRIFORME
Stump Puffball

DESCRIPTION: H: 1¼-3¼ in (3-8 cm), Ø: (1-4 cm.)
Pear-shaped fungus, consisting of a round, head, swollen at the top, in which a pore opens at maturity, and there is a large stipe which narrows toward the bottom which is no longer than the cap. It is creamy-white, later turning brown and covered in short, fragile spines. The base of the stipe is extended by long white, downy filaments which dig into worm-eaten wood. The flesh is white, turning olive green, except the lower part of the cap which remains white. Unpleasant odor, mild flavor.

sometimes half-buried. Fall through early winter. Fairly common.

HABITAT: In tufts on old logs and the rotten wood of various deciduous trees,

EDIBILITY
Edible but mediocre, only when young.

LYCOPERDON PERLATUM
Common Puffball

DESCRIPTION: H: 1¾-3¾ in (4-9 cm), Ø: 1¼-2¼ i in (3-6 cm).
More or less pear-shaped, creamy white and covered in little papillae of different sizes looking like tiny pearls, cream then ocher and finally olive-brown when the surface is smooth. The top opens at a perforation situated on one protuberance in the center of the cap. The stipe is largely splayed in a reverse

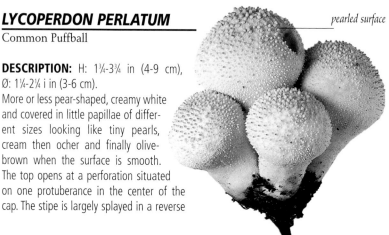

pearled surface

cone shape, and contains several folds. The flesh is white at first, becoming yellowish-brown, and tending to greenish-brown, eventually turning brown and powdery.

EDIBILITY

Edible when young and the flesh is still white but mediocre.

HABITAT: In dense clumps in deciduous or coniferous forests, more rarely in meadows. Summer through fall. Very common and widespread.

LYCOPERDON ECHINATUM

Spiny Puffball

DESCRIPTION: H: 1¼-2¾ in (3-7 cm), Ø: 1¼-2 in (3-5 cm).
Globe-shaped and carried on a very short stem thinning toward the base, entirely reddish-brown and covered with soft spines about ⅛ in (0.50 cm) long, in groups of three or four. The spines eventually fall off, leaving a reticulated surface. There is pore in the top which enables the spores to be released. The flesh is white and firm at first, then yellow-green, olive-brown, and finally powdery.

HABITAT: Beech forests on limestone soil. Fall. Uncommon.

long, soft spines

BOVISTA PLUMBEA
Leaden Puffball

DESCRIPTION: Ø: ½-¾ in (1-4 cm). Spherical and devoid of a stipe. The external envelope is thick and pure white, and peels away to reveal another interior covering that is lead gray, with a pore in the top. Flesh white then brown, and becoming powdery when mature.

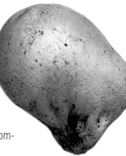

HABITAT: in small groups in meadows, pastures, and roadsides. Summer through fall. Fairly common.

SPECIAL FEATURES

The Leaden Puffball is only attached to the soil weakly, and when mature the first puff of wind can carry the whole fruiting-body far away, thus enabling it to disseminate its spores.

EDIBILITY
Edible when young, though poor.

CALVATIA UTRIFORMIS
Saddle-shaped Puffball

DESCRIPTION: H: 2-4¾ in (5-12 cm), Ø: 2-6 in (5-15 cm).

Fungus pear-shaped at first, with a white globulose top, covered in small pyramid-shaped warts which turn into a foma, leaving only their polygonal base behind. The fungus then turns gray-brown and the cap splits along its whole diameter. The bottom is barely wider than the top tapering at the base; it does not decay and can remain in the same place for several months with the base of the cap at the top, shaped like a small cup. The flesh is white and spongy, eventually turning yellowish-green, and finally olive-brown.

HABITAT: Lawns and orchards, especially in the mountains. Summer through early fall. Fairly common.

EDIBILITY
Edible when young, though poor.

CALVATIA EXCIPULIFORMIS

Pestle Puffball

DESCRIPTION: H: 2¾-7¼ in (7-18 cm), Ø: 2-4 in (5-10 cm).
Fungus consisting of two parts. The upper part is globulose, first white then soon turning ocher, and the lower part is the stipe. The upper part is soon covered with little soft, pointed warts which fall off rather quickly. The fungus splits across the width when mature, to release the spores. The stipe is half the width of the head and represents half the height of the fungus. It is wrinkled, folded, granulose, first white then ocher.

HABITAT: in meadows, well-lit woods of deciduous or coniferous trees and parks. Summer through fall. Uncommon to common.

LANGERMANIA GIGANTEA

Giant Puffball

DESCRIPTION: Ø: 6-6 in (15-40 cm).
Large round white shape, apparently resting on the ground, smooth but lumpy, pitted with shallow depressions, matt, later stained with ocher, velvety to the touch, like chamois leather. Flesh white, soft to spongy, yellowing, then turning olive-brown. Faint odor, mild, pleasant flavor.

HABITAT: singly or in groups, in parks, on lawns, beside hedgerows, often on nitrogenous soils. Summer through fall. Uncommon and grows again in the same places each year.

EDIBILITY

Edible when very young, though poor.

VASCELLUM PRATENSE

Meadow Puffball

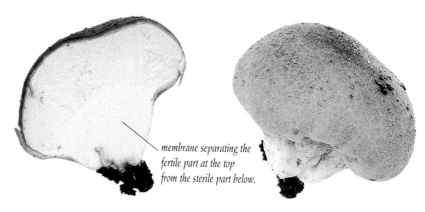

membrane separating the
fertile part at the top
from the sterile part below.

DESCRIPTION: Ø: ¾-2 in (2-5 cm).
Globulose, slightly flattened at the top,
white then ocher, finally pale brown upon
maturity. The surface is covered in tiny
warts which eventually disappear. The top
tears into one large opening through which
the spores escape in the form of a gray
dust. The stipe is very short or absent.
Flesh white and spongy in young
specimens then olive-brown and
powdery. If seen in vertical section,
the upper, fertile part can be seen to
be separated from the lower sterile
part by means of a membrane.

HABITAT: meadows, roadsides, lawns,
heaths. Summer through fall. Common.

small warts become detached,
revealing a smooth surface.

EDIBILITY

Edible young, while still white, but
rather mediocre.

SCLERODERMA CITRINUM, S. AURANTIUM

Common Earthball

DESCRIPTION: H: 1¼-3¼ in (3-8 cm), Ø: 1¼-4¾ in (3-12 cm). Globular fungus, flattened at the top, with a leathery envelope, pale yellow or orange-yellow and covered in small scales. Stem very short, whitish, with root-like filaments at the bottom which anchor the fungus to the soil. Flesh firm, dirty white becoming blackish and powdery upon maturity; strong, unpleasant odor.

HABITAT: in groups on bare ground among felled timber or on pathways, on moors, verges, or well-lit deciduous or coniferous woods, on acidic soil. Summer through fall. Very common and widespread.

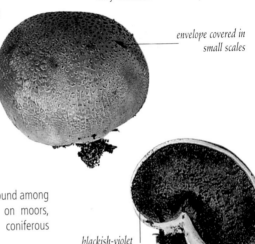

envelope covered in small scales

blackish-violet interior, marbled with white veins.

SPECIAL FEATURES

The flesh of the Common Earthball looks similar to that of the Black Truffle; it has thus been used fraudulently to imitate a truffle in certain foodstuffs, allegedly containing Black Truffles.

TOXICITY

Slightly poisonous.

CYATHUS STRIATUS

Bird's Nest Fungus

DESCRIPTION: H: ½-⅝ in (1-1.5 cm),
Ø: ¼-½ in (0.5-1 cm).
Vase or cup-shaped fungus, the top covered at first by a small white membrane that breaks open to reveal little white lentil-shaped grains that turns brown when mature, arranged in the bottom. The outer surface is brown and covered in stiff hairs; the inner surface is gray and bare but striated with vertical grooves.

HABITAT: in colonies consisting of large numbers of individuals on partially buried branches and twigs in damp woods. Summer through fall. Fairly common and widespread.

SPECIAL FEATURES

The spores are disseminated by the rain, whose drops detach the little grains containing the spores and disperse them.

membranous veil protects the little "eggs" before maturity

external brown fleecy coating

vertical interior grooves

CRUCIBULUM LAEVE, C. VULGARE, C. CRUCIBULIFORME
Orange Bird's Nest Fungus

DESCRIPTION: H: ¼-½ in (0.5-1 cm), Ø: ¼-½ in (0.5-1 cm).
The fruiting-body is egg-shaped in the young state, looking like the Bird's Nest Fungus, but the interior wall of the "nest" is smooth, not striated and pale ocher in color. The protective membrane covering young specimens is also ocher or orange, turning paler. The little grains (peridioles) inside are attached to the wall by short stalk.

HABITAT: grows in groups on various species of rotten wood in forests an parks, in summer and fall. Fairly common.

PHALLUS IMPUDICUS
The Stinkhorn

DESCRIPTION: H: 4-9 in (10-23 cm), Ø: 1-2 in (3-5 cm).
When very young, this fungus has the shape of egg about 2 in (5 cm) in diameter, with white filaments of mycelium at the base. The egg develops very rapidly and gives rise to a cap and stipe. The cap is conical, viscid at first and olive-green. The viscosity disappears, and the surface becomes white, pitted and porous, with sort of volva at the base, which is the remains of the membrane covering the egg. The strong, putrid odor can be detected from several yards away, and is a magnet for flies which feed on the mucus of the cap and thus disperse the spores.

HABITAT: in dispersed groups in deciduous or coniferous forests. Summer through fall. Very common.

EDIBILITY

If the sticky mass is removed, the egg, which does not have the nauseating smell, can be eaten, but is rather mediocre.

MUTINUS CANINUS
Dog Stinkhorn

DESCRIPTION: H: 3¼-6 in (8-15 cm),
Ø: ¼-½ in (1-1.5 cm).
The Dog Stinkhorn looks like a smaller version
of the Stinkhorn and it develops in the same
way. It is more slender and curved, and the cap
is the same width as the stipe. When the greenish mucus of the cap disappears, the underneath is seen to be honeycombed and red. The
stem is tinged with pink. The smell is not as
strong as that of the Stinkhorn but it is also
nauseating.

HABITAT: in groups in deciduous and coniferous forests, often near rotting stumps. Summer
through fall. Uncommon but tending to spread.

CLATHRUS RUBER
Red Cage Fungus

DESCRIPTION: H: 3¼-4¾ in (8-12 cm),
Ø: 2-3½ in (5-9 cm).
Starting from a whitish or yellowish egg, a
round, latticed fruit-body emerges. It is coral-
colored on the outside, the inside being covered in a greenish slime. The odor of the
mature fungus is that of rotting flesh.

HABITAT: in deciduous or coniferous woods,
parks, and gardens. From early summer
through fall. In warm or temperate zones.
Rather rare but found all over the world.

CLATHRUS ARCHERI

Red Tentacle Fungus

DESCRIPTION: Ø: 4-7¼ in (10-18 cm). The egg is whitish-gray to pinkish. It breaks open to reveal four to eight coral-red branches, stained with black, erect at first and joined at the bottom, which open like the petals of a flower. The smell becomes nauseating when the fungus is mature.

HABITAT: pastures, grass verges, hedgerows, clearings, under deciduous or coniferous trees. Late spring through fall. Rare through fairly common, distributed all over the world and tending to spread.

EDIBILITY

The "eggs" are edible but poor.

red branches stained with black

egg

SPECIAL FEATURES

The Red Tentacle Fungus is a native of Australia or New-Zealand. It appeared in Europe for the first time in 1914, in the Vosges mountains of France. It was almost certainly introduced, either on raw wool, or on imported armaments.

GLOSSARY

Adnate (gills or tubes): welded to the stipe along the entire width of the mushroom.

Appendiculate: margin of a cap to which fragments of veil adhere.

Armilla: covering which may be scaly and which covers the stipe of certain species, except in the upper part.

Basidiomycete: the biggest group of macrofungi, so-called because the spores are carried on club-shaped protrusions called basidia.

Basidiospore: spore of a basidiomycete.

Bulb: swollen base of the stipe of certain fungi.

Campanulate: bell-shaped, describing the shape of the cap.

Cerebriform: convoluted like a brain. The cap in species of Gyromitra (Brain Fungi) is cerebriform.

Cortina: partial veil consisting of very fine filaments covering the gills in a young specimen. As the mushroom grows, the cortina tears and persists only in the form of filaments on the cap and stipe.

Cuticle: coating of the upper surface of the cap (may be viscid, smooth, or fibrillose).

Decurrent (gills): which run down the stipe.

Deliquescent: liquifying when mature.

Fibrillose: covered in fine filaments or fibrils.

Fold, vein: sort of false gill under the cap of certain mushrooms, especially *Cantherellus* and *Craterellus*.

Free (gills): not attached to the stipe.

Fugaceous: disappearing more or less rapidly with age (a ring or cortina, for example).

Gelatinous: having the consistency of gelatin.

Gill: leaf-shaped appendage bearing the basidiospores on the underside of the cap of mushrooms of the basidiomyces family.

Globulose: spherical or almost spherical (as in the puffballs).

Humicolous: growing on humus.

Hygrophanous: changing color and appearance depending on the degree of atmospheric humidity.

Hymenium: the part of the sporophore or fruiting-body on which the spores are borne (gills, tubes, etc).

Inrolled (margin): rolled up at the edge (cap).

Latex: liquid in the flesh of certain fungi.

Lignicololous: growing on wood.

Margin: edge of cap or gills.

Marginate: bulb with a clear ridge around the top.

Milk: liquid exuded from the flesh of certain mushroms. *See* latex.

Mycelium: network of underground filaments which are the vegetative part of the fungus.

Mycorrhiza: close association between the mycelium of a mushroom and the roots of a higher plant (usually a tree).

Ostiole: small orifice from which spores can escape.

Partial veil: envelope covering the gills of a young fungus (which may persist in the form of a ring).

Pileus: word sometimes used to denote the cap of a fungus.

Pore: opening at the bottom of a tube (of a bolete, for example).

Pruinose: covered with bloom like a plum.

Pubescent: covered in fine hairs.

Reticulation: network of raised filaments on the stipe of certain boletes.

Rhizomorph, pseudorrhyza: Long root-like filaments of mycelium.

Ring: ring-shaped membrane around the center or top of certain mushrooms

Rooting: said of a stipe which extends deep into the soil by becoming thinner. the equivalent of a seed.

Sinuate (gills): with a dentation before they are attached to the stipe.

Spines: needle-shaped points, mainly under the cap of the Hedgehog Mushrooms (*Hydnum*).

Sporophore: visible part of the mushroom, also known as the fruiting body.

Spore: reproductive element in fungi,

Squamose: scaly.

Stipe: stem of the mushroom.

Symbiotic: said of a fungus that forms a relationship with a higher plant, from which both derive benefit.

Terricolous: growing on the ground (as opposed to lignicolous).

Tube: collection of small cylinders attached to the underside of certain fungi (such as boletes), through which spores are ejected at the bottom in an opening called a pore.

Umbilicate: with a clearly marked central narrow, ring-like depression.

Umbo: central mound protruding from the cap.

Umbonate: having an umbo.

Unequal: said of gills which are interspersed with gills of a shorter length.

Universal veil: envelope covering the whole of a young mushroom, sometimes persisting in the form of a volva at the base of the stipe or as scales on the cap.

Volva: envelope covering the base of the stipe of certain mushrooms, a remnant of the veil which covered the young fungus.

Waterlogged: gorged with water.

INDEX

The figures in Roman letters refer to running text; the numbers in **bold** refers to pages on which the subject is treated more generally. Names in Roman letters are the common name, .names in iitalics are the botanical or scientific name.